W9-DIJ-819

Praise for *The Price of Tomorrow*

"Is this time different? Most economists say 'no'—we've adapted to many technological revolutions before. In contrast, Jeff Booth says 'yes.' And thus begins a journey of ideas as he takes the reader on a tour de force, making his case for why that's so and sharing revelations from his personal relationships with tech industry leaders along the way. To harness the power of technology for good, we need to understand how it is linked to humanity. In a sweeping analysis that draws upon economics, science, innovation, politics, psychology, sociology, and business, Booth offers an intriguing thesis predicated on the deflationary impact of technological advancement coupled with increasingly easy credit. True to his impulse as an entrepreneur—a thinker, but also a doer—he concludes with a call to action. Business leaders, entrepreneurs, policy makers, and youth committed to working towards a brighter future should read this book."

AJAY AGRAWAL professor at the University of Toronto and founder of the Creative Destruction Lab

"As someone who understands the exponential rate at which technology is advancing, Jeff Booth has a unique ability to connect the dots to something bigger in this must-read book. Few books offer a more succinct, provocative, and enlightening view of the world as it is today, and what it could be tomorrow. Your world view will transform instantly."

SALIM ISMAIL founding executive director of Singularity University and bestselling author of *Exponential Organizations*

THE
PRICE
OF
TOMORROW

Why Deflation Is the Key
to an Abundant Future

JEFF BOOTH

STANLEY PRESS

Copyright © 2020 by Jeff Booth

All rights reserved. No part of this book may be reproduced, stored in a retrieval system or transmitted, in any form or by any means, without the prior written consent of the publisher or a licence from The Canadian Copyright Licensing Agency (Access Copyright). For a copyright licence, visit www.accesscopyright.ca or call toll free to 1-800-893-5777.

ISBN 978-1-9992574-0-8 (paperback)
ISBN 978-1-9992574-1-5 (ebook)

Published by Stanley Press

Produced by Page Two
www.pagetwo.com

Cover and interior design by Setareh Ashrafologhalai

www.thepriceoftomorrow.com

To the extraordinary people who have positively impacted my life.

CONTENTS

PREFACE

W E LIVE IN an extraordinary time, where there could be global prosperity. Perhaps not in the same way we think about it today, but global prosperity, nonetheless. Technological advances are happening faster than our ability to understand them. In a world that moves faster than we can imagine, we cannot afford to stand still. We cannot afford to cling to systems and pretend they are working because they did in an era before technology. Continuing on the existing path, without significant changes to the way we think about economics and the way we have constructed economies will ensure chaos. On this path, the price of tomorrow is set to explode. In this extraordinary time, it is not reasonable to believe that what will work in the future should necessarily be built on what worked in the past.

Who am I to be saying this? I'm someone who has an unearned advantage and wants to use it to help. I grew up with incredibly good fortune. I was born in Canada, a nation that consistently ranks at the top of international polls of best places to live. I grew up with amazing parents who loved and supported me and my brothers, parents who taught us right from wrong and constantly challenged our learning through vigorous debate. It was an upbringing that allowed me to see a different world than many people see and then build on the edge of that knowledge. It's not that I faced no adversity—we did not grow up wealthy, and I have experienced tremendous loss, the kind when it feels like everything is taken in an instant. But my upbringing drove a deep curiosity to learn from everyone around me; that helps me to consider the world as it might look like from others' points of view.

From a young age, I was always curious. Curious to know how the world worked and why it worked that way, and I was never afraid to ask a big or seemingly crazy question. Even with all of the distractions of life today, I still take time to read about fifty books per year. That curiosity, combined with a drive to create something better in the world, was the start of an incredible adventure as an entrepreneur, an adventure that has had me alongside and inside some of the top technology companies globally. An adventure that also allowed me to gain friendships and learnings in many countries all over the world.

As my friend Thuan Pham, the chief technology officer of Uber, recently said to me over breakfast, "I am a firm believer that talent is distributed evenly around the world, but opportunities are not." I wholeheartedly agree. If our success in life depends on what and how we learn, and the people and environment around us—and I believe it does—then I had a head start that not everyone in the world, or even everyone in developed countries, has access to.

I have been in the front seat for technology change for about twenty years. In 1999, my friend Rob Banks and I founded BuildDirect, a technology company that tried to simplify the building industry. Driving change in an industry not generally known for innovation and transparency was filled with lessons and many ups and downs—going from an idea to more than $500 million in market capitalization and a doubling of sales each year to swinging for the fences to build something even bigger (and ultimately failing). Leading a technology company for nearly twenty years, through the dotcom meltdown, the 2008 financial crisis, and many waves of technology disruption has given me a unique insight on the ever-changing world around us. The external challenges of building a business in times that are changing so fast were hair-raising enough, but they were trivial compared to the many things I learned about myself through the adventure.

Every one of the technology founders and leaders I have spent time with is determined to use technology to make a positive impact on the world. I believe it is a trait shared by most technology entrepreneurs. Beyond building their businesses into successes, they are determined to make the world a better place. They, like all of us, make mistakes, but common in every one of them is a genuine desire to help.

Most times, the entrepreneurial spark comes from envisioning the way the world could work versus the way it does now. In other words, the opportunity to create something better comes from observing something broken or that doesn't work the way you believe it should. That, oftentimes, creates the highs and lows of the entrepreneurial adventure because even if you are right, change is never easy. Many of history's greatest entrepreneurs, scientists, and leaders were ridiculed early on, but continued, because they saw something that needed change. That itch had to be scratched.

They, in turn, create their own reality—and ours with it. The truth is we all have that power. How we each view our own reality and the stories we tell ourselves about who we are determine many of the actions we choose. Those choices compound and sometimes we don't realize, or we forget, that we control our own thoughts, and we control our time. We all have choices on how and with whom to spend our time; it is one of the most important choices you can make.

Today, I am in the fortunate position to spend my time helping some of the most extraordinary technology entrepreneurs and their companies in diverse industries. From that vantage point, I have a rare view to many of the changes underway that promise a better tomorrow.

There is Karn Manhas, the founder and CEO of Terramera, who wondered why farming required toxic pesticides when for millennia plants have thrived in harsh environments. That question led him and his team to invent a technology that allowed organic compounds to outperform synthetic ones. Not only does this change the game for organic farming, when the technology is applied to synthetic pesticides, it reduces their use by up to 90 percent. Those same pesticides that we use on our food to kill insects end up in our bodies, so removing or reducing them is a big deal.

Understanding that home ownership is one of the most important wealth generators, Michael Stephenson and Steve Jagger set out on a mission to deliver home ownership to the 90 percent of people left out. Their company, Addy, uses technology to democratize this asset class and lets people own real estate for as little as a dollar. In a world that is becoming more unequal, giving access to a generation left out could help stem the tide.

Chonlak Mahasuvirachai is determined to build one of the largest marketplaces in Southeast Asia by simplifying the home-building industry. Frustrated by the lack of access and control for consumers, she chose to build NocNoc to bring far better choice, value, and simplicity than could otherwise be achieved. By designing the company around some of the platform principles shared in this book, the company is growing quickly—from just over a million in revenue in the second quarter of 2019 to over 55 million bhat in the third quarter.

These are just a select few of the leaders I have had the privilege of witnessing change their respective industries. Each of them is distinctive in their approach and market, but they have in common an unwavering drive to help people, and the companies are successful because they do. Almost every company I'm involved with is in some way using artificial intelligence to make better decisions. Many of the companies create success by removing massive inefficiency in the market. Unfortunately, projected forward, that comes at the expense of the jobs of today. For the companies and leaders that win, that will be very lucrative—but when you add up what is happening across the technology landscape, it means fewer winners and more losing out unless there are massive new industries created.

I am not a technology utopian: I don't believe that technology will solve all of our ills. Nor am I a technology dystopian: I don't believe that technology will ruin us. These are far too simple frameworks. The human condition cannot cope with either unilaterally. We would be unhappy and rebel in either case. In a world where there were no problems and technology did all of our bidding, we would quickly become bored and yearn for a problem to solve. In a more dystopian world where technology was used to control us, people would eventually rise up and fight that control. I do believe, though, that technology today is different than technology in the past.

The thesis of this book is something that I have been following closely for almost a decade, talking about it with family and friends and watching things unfold as expected—like signposts on a road, knowing what the next sign would say. At the same time, I was hoping I was wrong.

The scope of this book needed to be broad, while at the same time going deep enough in certain fields of research and technology to demonstrate patterns otherwise unseen. Choosing to write this book meant publicly challenging universal truths which many in our society believe—something that rarely wins popularity contests. But it is something I felt I must do, because technology changes the operating system of the world we live in. That operating system—the rules by which we have built our wealth and economies—will need an overhaul, and there has not been sufficient debate or dialogue. For reasons we will explore, instead of focusing on root-cause issues to fix, the dialogue is focused on second- and third-order effects of those root causes.

It's time we started asking bigger questions and then listening to the answers—not just for our future but that of our children.

INTRODUCTION:
THE END OF INFLATION

"The ideas of economists and political philosophers, both when they are right and when they are wrong, are more powerful than is commonly understood. Indeed the world is ruled by little else. Practical men, who believe themselves to be quite exempt from any intellectual influence, are usually the slaves of some defunct economist."

JOHN MAYNARD KEYNES *The General Theory of Employment, Interest and Money* (1936)

TECHNOLOGY IS DEFLATIONARY.

That is not conjecture. It is the nature of technology. And because technology underpins more and more of the world around us, it means that we are entering into an age of deflation unlike any the world has ever seen. We might not like what that means, or be ready for the changes that it foretells, but it doesn't change the facts.

Our economic systems were not built for a world driven by technology where prices keep falling. They were built for a pre-technology era when labour and capital were inextricably linked, an era that counted on growth and inflation, an era where we made money from scarcity and inefficiency. That era is over. But we keep on pretending that those economic systems still work.

We are at a critical point, because many of our choices are in fact choices about economics. Most choices come down to economic realities: a trade-off between our perceived value and price. We might aspire to be more environmentally minded while choosing to drive a car that is convenient for us and a toll on the environment. We may want all of our food to be organic but be unwilling or unable to pay the extra cost for it. Businesses are no different. A business is just a collection of people making choices with the aim of growing a better business while, at the same time, in competition with other businesses trying to do the same. "Better business" often comes down to the harsh realities of economics—or the value that the business brings to its users (whether that value is perceived or real). Those economic choices to compete and win more of scarce markets lead to almost everything else. From your income and lifestyle, to your opportunities for travel and leisure, to how you care for your family, economics is fundamental to it all.

Every so often, we learn something new that rewrites all of what we have come to know and trust. In those moments, our foundation of knowledge crumbles—and with it, many of the beliefs that we have built on top of it. Those transitions are hard because we do not easily let go of our beliefs.

We are at a crossroads. What worked before will not work in the future. Technology is moving too fast—and it will only move faster from here. Even if we wanted to, we can't put the genie back into the bottle. We need to build a new framework for our local and global economies, and soon, or the same technology that has the power to bring abundance to us and our world will instead destroy it.

The only thing driving growth in the world today is easy credit, which is being created at a pace that is hard to comprehend. The rise of that credit and corresponding debt is keeping us locked into a system where we are the proverbial frogs in a pot with the heat of the water slowly rising and we do not notice. And as we try to artificially drive an economic system built for the past, we are creating more than just economic trouble. On our current path, our world will become profoundly more polarized and unsafe.

The seemingly random events of Brexit, Trump, and a rise in populism and hate in our world are not haphazard or isolated at all. They are all connected to a loss in hope for a better future for large portions of the population. Underlying this loss of hope is a new economic reality where it's not just the poor who are missing out on economic gains. Much of the middle class is also feeling squeezed. Instead of technology allowing for a fifteen-hour work week, as Keynes predicted when he penned his 1930s essay "Economic Possibilities for Our Grandchildren," vast numbers of people are working longer, in jobs they rightly fear will soon be gone. Trapped—wondering how they will provide for their families and basic needs when the other shoe drops. At the same time, we are seeing a massive rise in inequality: in the United States, the top 5 percent of the population now holds more than two-thirds of the wealth, while the remaining 95 percent of the population fights for their share of the other third.[1] Just three people—Jeff Bezos, Bill Gates, and Warren Buffett—account for more wealth than 50 percent of the population.

It is easy to point at the wealthy and assign blame, but the focus should instead be on a broken system that reinforces radical inequality. In fact, many of the wealthiest families are aware of the very same risk to society and are intent on trying to fix it, either by entering the debate and making their voices heard and/or committing to philanthropy. The Giving Pledge, signed by 204 pledges at the time of writing, dedicates the majority of their wealth to giving back. But it shouldn't even be necessary.

The concentration of wealth has not been this high since the late 1920s. The world naturally becomes more unsafe when large amounts of people with increasing anxiety about their own economic future see incredible wealth creation in the hands of very few people. That environment provides fertile ground for revolutions. The loss in faith of systems meant to be reliable predictably leads to blame and division—all of which can be opportunistically redirected to target groups such as immigrants, religious groups, political parties, other countries, and so on. In other words, populism explodes because of an unjust system. It's hard not to look back to a similar loss of hope and rise in populism and ideologues around the world in the early 1930s, which escalated into World War II.

It is the same loss of hope that is driving elections today. Countries that once considered themselves enlightened are torn by ugly xenophobia, committed to protectionism and closing their borders. Entire populations are being swayed by politicians who incite more anger and polarization by creating "us versus them" narratives without understanding the root causes of our new reality. Many of them are using social media as a powerful weapon in their aim to consolidate power. They're building influential communities online that fuel dissension in the streets. In Germany, the far-right populist Alternative für Deutschland (AfD) went from zero seats in the 2013 election to forming the largest opposition party in that parliament in 2019. Around the world, authoritarian regimes are flourishing. The trend of more wealth inequality, more polarization, and more discord is a major threat to our collective future. And it is all being caused by the same thing: adherence to an economic system designed for a different time.

How did we end up here? And where are we going?

The age of inflation

All of our lives, we have lived in a world where hope for a better future was a motivating force in economics—a world where growth reigns. Our parents grew up in that same world, and so did their parents. It is what we know.

The American dream espouses the idea that no matter who you are, if you work hard enough or are innovative enough you can achieve almost anything you desire. Ever-higher-paying jobs are central to this construct. We expect to start our careers, earn more over time, and hopefully at the same time outrun rising prices. If we are lucky enough to have bought assets, the rising prices of those assets, because of inflation, creates longer-term wealth. If we leverage those assets by adding debt, our return is even greater because the asset increases in value while the dollars that we pay back in debt are priced in today's dollars—and with inflation, and growth in our incomes due to the inflation, we pay back the debt tomorrow in dollars that are worth less.

Housing is the classic example of this leverage. My parents bought their first house in suburban Vancouver, Canada, in 1977 for $69,000. At the time, it was a large sum of money for them. But with a down payment of $10,000 and a mortgage of $59,000, they were on their way to seeing the benefits of buying assets in an inflationary environment. Their incomes rose over the course of their careers, and with that rise in incomes, the mortgage of $59,000 became easier to pay. All the while, inflation also increased the value of their home: today it's worth about $1.5 million.

Almost any asset shares the same fundamental story, whether those assets are stocks, resources, or art. And there is nothing fundamentally wrong with the equation. It has driven enormous wealth and prosperity. True, asset owners have prospered more than others, which has contributed to inequality, but overall in the world, this process has driven much of the world out of poverty.

But what happens when we can't count on a system of growth and inflation anymore? What if a more powerful force renders most of our efforts to create inflation irrelevant? And what if, by desperately trying to cling to an outdated inflationary model, we drive more wealth inequality, more polarization, and more discord into our societies?

Today, we are in that scenario. The continual growth and inflation we expect—the system we've built our nations' economies around—is ceasing to exist. Technology is a deflationary force so great that, in the end, nothing we do will stop it.

The shrinking world of technology

I was given my first cellphone in 1988 as a gift from my employer as I left to start a new career. It was an incredibly special gift because it was completely unexpected. Cellphones in 1988 were quite rare, and the Motorola 8000 was one of the first to be truly portable—before that, they needed to be carried in suitcases. The phone was about the size and weight of a brick with a long antenna. It had thirty minutes of talk time before it needed to be charged for ten to twelve hours, and it cost about $2,000. My friends wanted to make calls from it just to say they were talking on a cellphone, and I tried to be careful how much I let them because calls cost $1.50 per minute. No text, no apps, no data, just phone calls—but that ability to make a call when I wanted to instead of trying to find a quarter and a pay phone was revolutionary. My first cellphone bill, with roaming charges, added up to about $1,200. I remember it distinctly because it was an insane amount of money at that time in my life. But for me in 1988, technology had finally arrived.

That was just over thirty years ago, and it is absolutely staggering how far we have come.

Take out your smartphone. How big is it? How much did it cost? How much does it cost to use? What can it do?

That same deflationary force made our phones cheaper and more powerful: it turned your phone into a camera, flashlight, a map, a measuring tape, a calendar, a wallet, a guitar tuner, and a million more things. All free or nearly free.

When we use technology, there is an exponential effect in its output or power relative to its price. We get far greater benefit and the price continues to fall. The abundance that it brings to our lives is incredible and it is all around us. In chapter 4, we will explore in depth what is underlying this extraordinary performance gain. But we only need to look at our phones to get a convincing picture of the deflationary effects of technology.

Deflation, put simply, is when you get more for your money— just as inflation is when you get less for your money. With deflation, a currency becomes more valuable because its buying power goes up in relation to goods and services. With inflation, it's the opposite: the prices of goods and services go up and therefore a currency's value is lower as purchasing power is less.

Deflation is not intrinsically good or bad. It just matters where you put your money. On each side of the equation, there are winners and losers. With inflation, holders of assets win, since the dollars in the future are worth less and it would therefore take more dollars to buy assets at a later date—like my parents and their first house. With deflation, holders of currency are the winners, since their dollars can buy more goods and services in the future than they could today.

The problem is that we still think that deflation is restricted to parts of our economy—that we will keep getting more with less in our electronic devices while getting the benefits of inflation in the rest of our lives. And we still look at technology through a narrow lens, as if it's only something that powers our phones.

Even zooming out a little more, we often think of the technology industry in terms of giants like Apple, Google, Microsoft, Facebook, Amazon, and, in China, Tencent, Baidu, and Alibaba. We often don't even realize that it is the same deflationary force in those companies that we are celebrating in using their services, often without even thinking about it. Whether it is the free and abundant information Google provides or the continued lower pricing and increasing service of Amazon, we continue to get more for less.

But technology has even wider and more important ramifications. Technology is not an industry isolated to our phones or Google searches or things we buy on Amazon. Technology is making its way into everything. It is increasingly the backbone of every industry and every company. In the near future, if you're not a technology-based company, you will likely not be a company at all.

So, if technology is making its way into every industry, why should we expect to get the benefit of the deflationary force in some places but inflation everywhere else? If the same technology that gave us abundance in our phones is now moving into just about every industry, should we not expect both abundance and price deflation in everything around us?

If everything—not just phones or Internet companies but *everything*—is giving far more performance and at the same time falling in price, a family that makes $75,000 this year and struggles to make ends meet could make $70,000 next year and the dollars would go further. And then $60,000 a few years after that and it would go further still, continuing to gain more for less with the natural deflationary trend in technology. That would allow us to step off the existing treadmill of chasing higher and higher prices, requiring ever-higher-paying jobs to keep up.

That may sound radical, but if technology is deflationary, and we expect technology to continue its advance into more and more industries, it may not be radical at all. It may be the only sane thing to do.

There's just one problem: if technology should be driving everything cheaper, why is life getting more expensive?

Reactionary economics

All over the world, rent, housing prices, fuel, food, and many other costs are rising, keeping us on a hamster wheel of work. To anyone living in this environment, it is almost impossible to believe in deflation or the abundance that might be possible with it.

But this rise in prices is artificial—driven by an enormous rise in credit and debt.

Governments and central banks will do almost anything to stop deflation. Inflation targets, set at typically 2 percent, are public elements of their mandates, with a blend of ever-increasing, wild ideas to keep inflation going. Any real growth that the world has seen is only because of an unprecedented spending spree fuelled by easy credit and debt that masks what is really happening underneath. The problem comes from believing we can outrun deflation and the natural order of things by creating more and more debt. It's a bit like trying to flap your arms to fight gravity: gravity will win. Even a plane using massive energy to stay in the air must eventually land.

In measuring the amount of debt in the world, it is important to compare the total debt of governments, persons, or corporations in relation to its impact on total growth of gross domestic product (GDP). Otherwise, one can be easily fooled by sleight of hand of slower growth of debt in one part of the economy that is offset by debt increasing quickly in another. For example, a government brings its debt under control by no longer funding a program, but that stop in funding forces debt to accumulate faster in consumers who need the program; only through total debt will you see the real impact on GDP.

There is already too much debt in the world, which paradoxically makes the problem harder to solve. Debt combined with deflation is a toxic combination, because borrowers have to pay the same for their interest payments while earning less. This raises the real value of the debt, making it more unlikely to ever be paid back. Defaults soar and credit is destroyed, leading to severe depressions in economies.

In 2000, the total debt in the world was approximately US$62 trillion. At the same time, the world economy in 2000 was about US$33.5 trillion. Since 2000, the world economy has grown from US$33.5 trillion to about US$80 trillion, but to achieve that growth, the total debt has grown to over US$247 trillion as of the third quarter of 2018, according to the Institute of International Finance. In other words, it has taken approximately $185 trillion of global debt to achieve $46 trillion of global growth.

If we stopped adding to that debt and started to pay it back at a rate of $1,000 per second, it would take nearly 8,000 years. Instead, we keep adding to it. And it gets even worse—if it took creating $185 trillion of debt to get only $46 trillion of growth, I'll show you in chapter 4 why it will take at least double that amount of debt to get another $46 trillion of growth.

I can't imagine going to the bank for a loan and pitching this great idea where I would add $4.00 of debt for every $1.00 of growth. Even if I taxed the entire $1.00 gain at 100 percent, the $1.00 would never allow me to pay back my original loan. The mirage of growth today is nothing more than a debt-fuelled spending binge.

Debt-fuelled spending is not always bad. Often, debt can be used to grow wisely by funding smart long-term investments. A business that takes on debt to invest in automation gains more leverage against its competitors and can pay back that debt with a better return to the business in the future thanks to that automation. But when a business continues to spend more than it earns, or invests its debt in things that do not provide an economic return, the debt becomes a weight on future growth as current dollars need to be allocated to pay the servicing cost of the interest or payments. At some point, the weight of the debt becomes unbearable, and the business is forced to restructure or close—which wipes out all of the debt, in turn harming those it's owed to.

Overall, an economy is the same. An economy can grow faster because of that same leverage or credit applied to it, pulling demand forward by increasing what can be spent today at the expense of paying for it tomorrow. People and households have more money, so they spend more money and businesses and economies grow at a faster rate. But that money needs to be repaid... one way or another.

Is it any wonder that the biggest movers in financial markets today are betting not on the growth of companies but instead on the direction of central bankers and governments with regard to monetary policy? On one side, we have this incredible deflationary force driven by technology, and on the other side, we have a force trying to stop it. That force is a money printing machine.

In his book *Principles for Navigating Big Debt Crises*, Ray Dalio, through much research and market knowledge, uses data from previous debt crises to examine what the implications are to government policy when debt gets out of hand. Dalio does an incredible job of distilling the complexity of markets into an easy-to-understand and valuable read. When debt gets too large, in his words:

There are four levers that policy makers can pull to bring debt and service levels down to income and cash flows that are required to service them:

1. Austerity—spending less

2. Debt defaults/restructuring

3. The central bank printing money or other guarantees

4. Transfers of money from those who have more than they need to those who have less (much higher taxes for the rich)[2]

Dalio concludes that in the end, "Policy makers always print. That is because austerity causes more pain than benefit, big restructurings wipe out too much wealth too fast, and transfers of wealth from haves to have nots don't happen in sufficient size without revolution."[3] And I agree with Dalio that it is highly likely that policy makers will print again as governments around the world try to kick the can down the road once more. I just do not believe that is the right solution this time. It will only make things worse.

What no historical record of previous debt crises could show is the incredible deflationary force of technology. It is different from historical transitions like the Industrial Revolution, and moreover, it has only barely started. Most of the deflation is still in front of us. That deflationary force, combined with a global market where all state actors need to drive growth and higher paying jobs in their own economies, sets us up for a future without precedent. Where the rules need to be rewritten.

Technology itself is neither good nor evil. Neither are the deflationary effects it brings with it. Our systems of governance determine how it is used. At least for today, technology is designed by humans and can be used to do immense good in the world, bringing abundance: a world where we all receive far more for less. But today, it is difficult for any individual, let alone those outside the technology industry, to keep up with the rate of technology growth. We can fully expect that the technology that we see around us today will be primitive compared to what is just around the corner. We are starting to play a whole new game, one where many rules are the opposite of what we are used to.

Every game has winners and losers. It is similar if we look at the game of life: some people win more than others, and that is okay. Passion, risks, ingenuity, hard work, and smarts should be rewarded. The monumental challenges for any society are when an economic game is rigged in favour of a few while others are disadvantaged. When the disadvantaged realize that they are playing a game that cannot be won.

That is where we are in the world today, and even if most people don't realize why, discontent is rising. Owners of assets and those who have access to debt and leverage have been tremendous winners. So have technology companies that are using it to create monopolies bigger than was possible in the past. But it is coming at a cost. The cost is the populism that is rising around the world. And that cost is set to explode.

In the rest of this book, I'll look in depth at the situation: how we got here, where we're set to go from here, and what we can do about it. Prepare to be challenged.

1

HOW THE ECONOMY WORKS, PART I: PRINTING MONEY

HAD DINNER RECENTLY with Chen Fong, a friend of mine from the Creative Destruction Lab, where we mentor, invest, and advise numerous technology startups. He is also a professor emeritus at the Faculty of Medicine at the University of Calgary, cofounder of Calgary Scientific, and a member of the Order of Canada. In addition to the fifty or so companies that Chen mentors and invests in, he still finds the time to sit on six charitable boards. To say the least, it was a very engaging evening with a deep thinker. During dinner and after a few glasses of wine, the talk turned to rising inequality around the world. Chen shared a story with me about his in-laws.

It was shortly after the 2008 financial crisis. Chen had no reason to expect his in-laws were worried. They were in their eighties and they were financially secure. The crash had not hurt their lifestyle. But they watched the response to the crisis from governments around the world, and they remembered what they had seen before. He asked them why they were worried. Their answer stayed with him:

"First currency wars, then trade wars, then real wars."

Perhaps what Chen's parents-in-law saw was the repeat of a scenario that gave rise to extremism, political upheaval, and ultimately a world war about eighty years ago. That scenario was rising inequality and a loss of hope in large segments of a population, which allowed new politicians to use that wedge to polarize, driving protectionism and nationalism.

What the experts got wrong

We know that 2008 wasn't any garden variety economic downturn. It also wasn't one that most of the economic establishment saw coming. The experts expected the world to continue in the manner in which they were accustomed until they were well past the edge of the cliff:

November 15, 2005

"With respect to their safety, derivatives, for the most part, are traded among very sophisticated financial institutions and individuals who have considerable incentive to understand them and to use them properly. The Federal Reserve's responsibility is to make sure that the institutions it regulates have good systems and good procedures for ensuring that their derivatives portfolios are well managed and do not create excessive risk in their institutions."

BEN BERNANKE Senate confirmation hearing

November 15, 2005

"We've never had a decline in house prices on a nationwide basis. So, what I think what is more likely is that house prices will slow, maybe stabilize, might slow consumption spending a bit. I don't think it's gonna drive the economy too far from its full employment path, though."

BEN BERNANKE interview with CNBC

February 14, 2007

"The weakness in housing market activity and the slower appreciation of house prices do not seem to have spilled over to any significant extent to other sectors of the economy."

BEN BERNANKE semi-annual Monetary Policy Report to the Congress

May 17, 2007

"We do not expect significant spillovers from the subprime market to the rest of the economy or to the financial system."

BEN BERNANKE speech in Chicago

September 4, 2007

"It is not the responsibility of the Federal Reserve—nor would it be appropriate—to protect lenders and investors from the consequences of their financial decisions."

BEN BERNANKE interview with CNBC

January 10, 2008

"The Federal Reserve is not currently forecasting a recession."

BEN BERNANKE interview with CNBC

July 16, 2008

"Fannie Mae and Freddie Mac are well capitalized and in no danger of failing."

BEN BERNANKE speaking to Congress

September 18, 2008

"We are in danger of a broad systemic collapse, and action needs to be taken urgently to head it off. We need the authority to spend several hundred billion."

HANK PAULSON in Oval Office

September 18, 2008

"The kind of financial collapse that we're now on the brink of is always followed by a deep, long recession... If we aren't able to head this off, the next generation of economists will be writing not about the thirties but about this."

BEN BERNANKE in Oval Office

October 28, 2008

"The downward trajectory of economic data has been hair-raising. It is becoming abundantly clear that we are in the midst of a serious global meltdown."

JANET YELLEN Federal Reserve transcripts[4]

One of the few economists to correctly forecast what was happening at the time was Nouriel Roubini, an economics professor at New York University. In 2006, two years before the collapse of Lehman Brothers and the rescue of the financial system, Roubini "stood before an audience of economists at the International Monetary Fund and announced that a crisis was brewing."

In the coming months and years, he warned, the United States was likely to face a once-in-a-lifetime housing bust, an oil shock, sharply declining consumer confidence and, ultimately, a deep recession. He laid out a bleak sequence of events: homeowners defaulting on mortgages, trillions of dollars of mortgage-backed securities unraveling worldwide, and the global financial system shuddering to a halt. These developments, he went on, could cripple or destroy hedge funds, investment banks, and other major financial institutions like Fannie Mae and Freddie Mac.[5]

To be fair, Roubini had missed recession calls in the past. But he was right about this one. Years of loose credit coupled with financial engineering wizardry created an unprecedented bubble in housing in the United States. When housing started to unwind, the interconnections that caused the run-up unwound as well. Those interconnections were global in nature and risked taking down the entire economic system.

It wasn't housing itself that caused the 2008 bubble. If it hadn't been housing, it would have been somewhere else that easy credit was flowing to. The continuing rise of debt that cannot be paid back was at the heart of the housing crises and will be at the heart of the next crisis. A bubble pops when people wake up and realize that the debt can never be paid off. At that point, credit is removed—and because easy credit was the main thing causing the run-up, assets collapse. It is what led to the bubble in technology stocks in early 2000s. It is what led to the crisis in Greece and to the crisis in Venezuela today.

Many people believe that the system is much safer now. That we have safeguards with financial controls to protect against a collapse like 2008. That the cause is well understood— low-income loans to housing and toxic assets tied to it. If you believe that, take another look at the timeline above to see what the experts were saying in the run-up to that crisis. While housing itself might be safer, the system is not.

With credit continuing to advance globally, it is only a shell game as to where the next crisis originates. In fact, the shell game is now moving to currencies themselves and the entire economic system that is built on top of them.

A financial system based on credit is just an exchange of money today for money later. I give you dollars today and temporarily lose the utility of my money in exchange for having more later. You have the inverse: the benefit of more money today and less tomorrow as you pay back the loan with interest.

This system works on trust—trust that you will pay what you said you would pay. It is the same whether that trust is in a person, company, or government. Remove trust and it affects the credit-worthiness of an individual or company. Remove trust from a system and the entire system can unravel very quickly.

The world in balance

World economies could be viewed as one large economy, driven by trust, interconnection, movement of money, and debt. That means that no single country's gross domestic product (GDP) can be considered in isolation.

There are four components that make up GDP:[6]

1. Consumer spending or personal consumption (C)
2. Investments (I)
3. Net exports (X)
4. Government spending (G)

The mathematical formula to calculate the components of GDP (Y) is simple: $Y = C + I + X + G$. GDP comes down to the interplay of those four components. Countries rely primarily on different levels because the inputs compete against each other. GDP tells you how each country is managing the four inputs together. As a by-product of that, it also tells you what a government values more to drive their economy and jobs. Higher-income countries typically rely on consumer spending as a primary driver of GDP growth, while lower-income countries are more likely to depend on net exports. These inputs compete against each other: for example, in countries with higher incomes, consumer spending naturally increases, but because their jobs pay more, their exports to other countries are disadvantaged by being more expensive.

This also means that when politicians talk of trade surpluses or deficits with their trading partners while only understanding one part of the equation, it's complete nonsense. Mathematically, the world's trade balance must be zero: for every buyer, there needs to be a seller, and for every seller, there needs to be a buyer.

Let's look at the trade relationship between the United States and China as an example. China runs a trade deficit with the United States, meaning that the United States imports more from China than it exports. Many, including the current president of the US, claim this is unfair.

Here is how the balance between the two countries actually works out. Almost 70 percent of the United States' GDP is made up of consumer spending; in China, consumer spending makes up only about 30 percent of GDP. In China, incentivizing production requires keeping lower wages (relative to the world), tax incentives for production and distribution, and investments in automation to achieve production that allows their exports to win on a world market. Conversely, to support consumer spending at 70 percent of the economy, the United States requires relatively higher wages, high credit creation with low interest rates (debt to finance that increased spending), and lower taxes. Donald Trump's tax incentives enacted November 2, 2017, had an effect of 1) increasing consumer spending and growth in the economy—in other words, I will give you more money, so you spend it, driving short-term growth in GDP and jobs; this 2) increased the trade deficit with China as consumers bought more imported products, and it also 3) increased the US budget deficit in 2018 to almost $800 billion. Over ten years, the Congressional Budget Office estimates that the tax cuts alone will add an additional $2.28 trillion of national debt to the US.

So each country is maintaining policies that incentivize its side of the equation with government help. If any of those variables changes too quickly in either economy, chaos ensues as the major part of their respective economies collapse.

Understanding this balance and making informed decisions is important because we all live in the same world; each side of a relationship affects the other. A growing consumer class in China could very well help lift world economies, but for that to happen, Chinese workers will need to be paid more. And if American workers want to sell to China, they'll have to earn less. I'm sure that many people in the US who are frustrated with China's role as producer would not accept the 996 work weeks (9 a.m. to 9 p.m., six days per week) for average wages of $1,400 per month that many of their Chinese counterparts have.

This same balance is seen around the world. When the European Union adopted a common currency, the euro gave increased purchasing power to Greece, Italy, Spain, Portugal, and others that previously had lower valued currencies. People in Greece, for example, were able to buy more from Germany, which is the third-largest exporter in the world. German banks were happy to fund loans to Greece, and both countries grew their GDP quickly—one because of exports, and the other because of consumer spending. German banks were giving Greece German money to buy from Germany, with the expectation that Germany would later get even more money back—which Greece would have to come up with somehow. When it was realized that Greece might not be able to pay back the money, Greece was forced into a crisis. Had Greece walked away from the loans, it wasn't only Greece that would suffer. The German banks underwriting the loans would have to write them off, causing Germany's economy to slow.

This is also happening between China and the US, and not in the way you might think. China has been buying US government debt as a consequence of trade. It now has more than $1.1 trillion of US reserves and tops the global list of US Treasury bond holders. As with Germany lending money to Greece, this can be looked at as vendor financing, such as you might get from a car dealer: I provide you cheap capital so that you purchase my goods, and I make more in the long run. It also helps to ensure a US market for China's exports by keeping interest rates low, so that consumers spend more. But China cannot reasonably stop buying government bonds without collapsing its own economy, because then interest rates would move much higher in the US and cripple consumer spending, which would then collapse China's economy. It's a feedback loop in interconnected economies.

And without continued debt-fuelled spending, it would be like sticking a pin in a balloon, because growth would collapse and we would suddenly see what has been there all along. The natural trend of technology deflation.

When economies and high-paying jobs are at risk, though, the easiest thing to do in politics is to blame outsiders or game the situation to provide short-term benefit—and kick the can down the road. This ignores the impact of technological growth and only serves to create more global tension. Bringing back coal mining jobs at a time when hydrocarbons are being replaced by renewable energy is akin to training more blacksmiths when the horse and buggy was being replaced by the automobile. It doesn't address the root cause for the jobs disappearing: technology. It also doesn't allow focus on the most important jobs or things that must be done to enable the future.

Looking outward for blame also ignores decades of government policy that has seen most countries' government debt far too high already, continuing to grow much faster than their economies, setting up an untenable situation where servicing the debt is an increasing drag on the economies—and will ultimately become impossible.

The Ponzi economy

In his book *Between Debt and the Devil*, Adair Turner, the former chair of the Financial Services Authority in the United Kingdom, which regulated the financial services industry, takes readers down the path of unfettered borrowing by companies and individuals who are financing that borrowing not by creating more goods and services, but by relying on the price inflation of the assets they already have. This, in turn, fuels asset price inflation, people pile on more debt, and, like hamsters on a wheel, they keep going and going around until they fly off or collapse.

When debt is growing much faster than a country's economy, at what point does the music stop? It is often difficult to see, because asset price inflation can make individuals, companies, and even countries feel much better off than they are. In the run-up to 2008, the economy seemed very strong as individuals in the United States used the newfound gain in their home's asset value to take loans for cars, boats, and vacations. But when the asset (in this case, the home) falls in value, the debt still needs to be paid. We fool ourselves into believing that assets, such as stocks or housing, always go up over the long term because they always have. We should ask whether those same assets would have gone up over the last twenty years if there hadn't been $185 trillion of new capital injected into economies over that time. When that stops, which it eventually will, things will change very quickly.

If it takes ever-increasing credit growth to achieve economic growth, how are our economies any different from a

Ponzi scheme? A Ponzi scheme creates an illusion of profits because it pays early investors with investments from later investors. Even though the scheme is a fraud, it can look like a good business in that early investors talk about how great their returns are. Because it requires more and more capital to pay out investors, it continues until new investors at the bottom of the pyramid slow down enough to stop paying out earlier investors, which brings the entire system down. At what point does debt slow enough to bring the entire system down? When does the future stop paying off the past?

To keep the system running, monetary policy all around the world has target inflation rates. From a debt perspective, this makes sense: inflation makes debt easier to pay back because you're paying yesterday, when dollars cost more, with money from tomorrow, when dollars are worth less. In the United States in 1970, a $3.25 per hour wage had the same purchasing power as a $25.00 per hour job today. A movie ticket that cost $1.55 in 1970 is more than $9.00 today. A gallon of gasoline in 1970 was 36 cents; it's $2.98 today. A debt that you took on then that cost you 100 hours of work—$325—could be paid off with 13 hours of work today. Even with interest, you can come out ahead.

For those unable to access debt, though, and put it into assets that rose in value, the inflation has been punishing because their dollars do not go as far as they used to.

And since inflation makes your currency worth less over time, we need to start asking: Isn't currency founded on trust in the value of that currency? And doesn't that mean that by setting inflation target rates, governments have a stated goal of eroding that trust?

Cheap money

What can we do about this? Let's look at the 2008 crisis to help understand what can happen.

In an interconnected economy driven by credit and ever more debt, there are no easy choices. Once housing prices had collapsed, governments could 1) bail out the banks and the risk takers, and create moral hazard in doing so, or 2) risk a worldwide depression as trust in the financial system broke down and markets stopped. They chose door number one: bail out the banks and risk takers and create moral hazard in doing so.

We have no way of truly knowing how wide and lasting the damage would have been had the governments and central banks of the world not stepped in with massive support to save the economic system. We can play armchair quarterback now, but policy makers at the time were dealing with real-time changes and without all of the facts in an interconnected global economy that could have ground to a halt causing much more damage than we can imagine. They knew every decision would be put under a microscope and questioned for generations.

That said, they made a choice that changed capitalism by gifting many of the engineers of the chaos with risk-free returns at the taxpayers' expense. Using quantitative easing in the United States and other monetary easing around the world, central banks and governments decided who won and who lost. And it is the second- and third-order effects of that decision that are sowing the seeds of discontent around the world.

Quantitative easing refers to the act of injecting liquidity into an economy by a central bank. In order to inject liquidity, new dollars need to be created and they need to be delivered into the economy. Many people refer to the first part as "printing new money," though the money does not actually need to be printed—it can just be given as balance sheet credits by a central bank. For instance, the US Federal Reserve's balance sheet has expanded from just under $900 billion in 2008 to approximately $4 trillion today.

The second part, delivering the newly created money into the economy, is done in a variety of ways, such as large-scale asset purchases from public and private sectors like the Troubled Asset Relief Program, where the government buys toxic or underperforming assets. By doing so, governments take bad assets off the balance sheets of corporations and give them fresh new capital instead.

Another way to get new money into the system is through directly issuing loans to commercial banks. In the United States in 2008, banks were given access to borrow federal funds at a 0 percent interest rate. The banks could then lend out those dollars at higher interest rates to rebuild their damaged balance sheets over time. Some non-banks at the time, like Morgan Stanley and Goldman Sachs, changed their charters to become banks to get access to the free money as well. Without this opportunity, many of the banks and investments banks would have merged, been bought at pennies on the dollar, or collapsed outright.

By nature, though, quantitative easing also causes currency devaluation, even if that's not what it's specifically intended to do. The government doesn't actually have more assets; it's just representing its assets with more units of currency, which means each unit of currency is worth less—like cutting a pizza into twelve slices instead of eight, or dividing an estate between ten heirs rather than nine. Immediately following the announcement of the first round of quantitative easing, the US dollar lost value, and other currencies where easing was prominent also fell and remained in equilibrium to the US dollar. As a result, if you were a holder of US dollars or cash, you lost value. If you were paid in US dollars, your pay was worth less—although you probably didn't notice it until your fuel prices went up in relation to your paycheque. As the US currency became weaker, asset prices around the world rose in lockstep.

Oil prices are a good example to demonstrate this, because oil is an asset with limited supply. If a country's currency loses value and the country needs to import oil, it needs to use more of that currency to buy the same amount of oil. Through three rounds of quantitative easing in the United States, oil prices rose from $30 a barrel to more than $100. Countries with strong natural resource sectors that are in limited supply saw their currencies' value rise in tandem with the easing in the United States. For example, in my own country, Canada, natural resources are abundant; oil, gold, lumber, and other commodities are major drivers of the economy. The

Canadian dollar, which typically trades at around 75 cents to the US dollar, rose to almost a record high versus the US dollar after 2008. Other countries with large natural resource sectors—like Brazil, Russia, and Saudi Arabia—also saw their currencies rise. And along with that, their own labour rates also rose relative to the US.

There is a close connection between currency value and labour rate—how much workers are paid. A country that devalues its currency also indirectly lowers its labour rate against global competitors, which can help some job growth in the short term, because its goods cost less to buyers in other countries. For example, if the Thai baht goes down in value compared to the US dollar and Thai workers are still paid the same, goods that Thailand produces cost US customers less, which can help jobs in Thailand in the short term because more US customers will buy those goods. But the costs for Thai workers for all imported goods they need to buy may go up in direct proportion to the currency devaluation.

Countries often devalue currency to help their export markets. But in a globally connected world with many countries driving each of their own national interests and jobs, this makes less sense. Other countries trying to compete for the same scarce jobs devalue their currencies to keep their economies from collapsing. This race to the bottom on currencies only serves to further push up global asset prices. And the endless game of reducing the value of currencies relative to others only serves as a short-term panacea, because asset prices will rise far more quickly than jobs can be created—and pay rates increased—to keep pace with the asset price rise.

As the economist John Maynard Keynes wrote,

> Lenin is said to have declared that the best way to destroy the capitalist system was to debauch the currency. By a continuing process of inflation, governments can confiscate, secretly and unobserved, an important part of the wealth of their citizens. By this method they not only confiscate, but they confiscate arbitrarily; and, while the process impoverishes many, it actually enriches some. The sight of this arbitrary rearrangement of riches strikes not only at security, but at confidence in the equity of the existing distribution of wealth. Those to whom the system brings windfalls, beyond their desserts and even beyond their expectations or desires, become "profiteers," who are the object of the hatred of the bourgeoisie, whom the inflationism has impoverished, not less than of the proletariat. As the inflation proceeds and the real value of the currency fluctuates wildly from month to month, all permanent relations between debtors and creditors, which form the ultimate foundation of capitalism, become so utterly disordered as to be almost meaningless; and the process of wealth-getting degenerates into a gamble and a lottery.[7]

Changing the rules

When governments are unable to substantively change the rules of the game or gain leverage because other countries are forced to devalue in response to keep their jobs, the next step—as foretold by Chen's parents-in-law—is tariffs and trade wars.

Many politicians around the world are gaining power on promises of closing borders, including Donald Trump, who was elected on a protectionist America-first platform. He also promised to erase a trade deficit with China, only to see it continue to rise to its highest level. And a favourite weapon in his arsenal is tariffs.

Could tariffs help?

The last time tariffs were enacted in a major way in the United States, it didn't end well. In the 1930s, the US had a similar goal as many countries have today. An unwind of credit expansion around the world created the Great Depression. To protect American farming jobs from foreign competition, the US passed the Smoot-Hawley Tariff Act, named after the congressmen who conceived it. That act raised tariffs to protect jobs but dramatically underestimated the reaction from other countries in doing so. They were foolish to believe that they could keep their existing exports while protecting their own economy from imports. The resulting trade wars, with Canada and Europe retaliating and increasing tariffs on US goods, are widely understood to have prolonged the Great Depression and made it worse for the very farmers that the tariff act was supposed to protect.

We see the same thing happening around the world today as each country retaliates in its own way. Our economies and countries are interconnected, as are our people. No country works in isolation.

Is there any other option?

Let's imagine for a moment a world where the central bankers decided to let the banks fail, something that many say should have been the right course—capitalism actually calls for such a cleansing. At the end of 2008, there are no bailouts. No quantitative easing. It's not a difficult thought experiment.

Asset prices collapse. Loans on those assets become non-performing. Most of the banking system collapses. Only the best loans can be repaid. Many people are wiped out as the collapse destroys all who took unnecessary risks. Some of those are you and me and pensioners, people who misunderstood the risk we were taking with some of the exotic investments that we were told were safe. As well, many more are wiped out because of the lack of liquidity in the system, meaning that some investments deemed safe also fail. This result might produce a depression so severe it would make the Great Depression look like a walk in the park. But in that environment, hard dollars would explode in value and those who had savings and cash would pick up extremely low-priced assets and mispriced deals and make their fortunes.

Imagine how different your life could look. Real estate would not be priced anywhere near where it is today. Stocks would likely still be near historic lows. Our politicians would look different—in fact, some of them wouldn't be our politicians, because they would have been wiped out with their debt and the asset price collapse.

Monetary easing and artificially low interest rates have been a grand experiment played out on the world stage without full consideration of the downstream effects. For the wealthy and those with assets that have been artificially boosted, that experiment has played out well. If we're being honest with ourselves, much of the wealth and privilege that we enjoy is not from our ingenuity or hard work, but because the governments of the world decided to print money. Our assets, including real estate and stocks, were the beneficiaries, having run up in value far beyond what they would have been without the printing.

Meanwhile, those without assets find themselves on a treadmill that is moving ever faster—and unable to keep up.

It's like we're living in Bizarro World where everything is backwards. *Bizarro*—a comic created by Dan Piraro—takes place not on a spherical Earth but on a cube-shaped Htrae (Earth spelled backwards). In one *Bizarro* strip from April 1961, a salesman is doing a brisk trade selling Bizarro bonds that are "guaranteed to lose money for you." That's not even a joke today. In many parts of the world, banks have negative rates: money retains more value stored under your mattress than in a bank.

So, as the market celebrates ever more stimulation from governments and stocks and housing continue to rise higher, the market should also "celebrate" the dislocation of our societies. As Paul Volcker, former chairman of the Federal Reserve, said in 2018, "The central issue is we're developing into a plutocracy. We've got an enormous number of enormously rich people that have convinced themselves that they're rich because they're smart and constructive."[8]

I grew up in a world where I believed anything was possible, and that hard work and ingenuity were rewarded. I still believe that. I also believe in capitalism, where risk is rewarded *and* punished, and where the free market is the ultimate referee of your value. That is why it pains me so much to see it breaking down. A market where government reaches in to decide who wins or loses is nothing more than crony capitalism, where wealth is not created by the value you create and the risks you take to get there but by a political system that rewards its insiders.

And for every person on the winning side of that decision, there are many others on the losing side. Their costs of food, shelter, gas, and healthcare are rising because their cash and wages are less valuable. Assets that they don't yet own are running away in price. They are feeling the squeeze of an unjust system.

Just like you, they might be unaware of how much was given to you in this exchange, and just like you, they are equally unaware of how much was taken from them. But they do know that something doesn't feel right—and they are fed up.

2

HOW THE ECONOMY WORKS, PART II: CREATIVE DESTRUCTION

T HE BIGGEST PROBLEM with all of the solutions we're trying today is that the inflationary environment that we have counted on for growth is breaking down because of technology. No tariffs, manipulation of currencies, or debt escalation will solve that problem. And as our economies move into the digital age where technology and data underlie everything, they don't just deflate, they also become increasingly interconnected. Information doesn't have the same constraints that physical goods have: it travels seamlessly across borders. It is much more efficient, eradicating a lot of waste from the system. But much of that waste and inefficiency are our jobs.

We have been told this before—only to prosper as technology and innovation transitioned some jobs but, overall, had a positive long-term impact on jobs and economies. In the 1800s, machines replaced much of the hard labour that came before them and society was enriched. That technology created more new jobs than it destroyed, and the luddites who feared that it would be the end of work were proven wrong. Or, maybe, they were just early.

Around the world, tensions are rising because prices are rising and high-paying jobs are at risk. A 2019 Pew Research Center study confirms the mood. Only 14 percent of US adults say that by the year 2050, the average working person in the US will have more job security.[9]

Because of this tension and fear, people are losing empathy and following xenophobic ideologues, and we are collectively missing the most important point: it is our inflationary system, which requires ever more jobs, that needs to be changed.

Out with the old, in with the new

One of the pillars of capitalism is a free-market system—it's the centrepiece of how all modern economies evolve—a near-constant flow of innovative entrepreneurs breaking monopolies and then themselves creating new ones. The paradoxical term "creative destruction" was coined for this by Austrian American economist Joseph Schumpeter (1883–1950). In Schumpeter's vision of capitalism, innovation by entrepreneurs was the disruptive force that sustained economic growth, even though it destroyed the value of established companies. Furthermore, the value that was destroyed in established companies was that which they enjoyed from some level of monopoly power derived from a previous technological, regulatory, organizational, or economic paradigm.

New technologies often change what is valuable in a way that is misunderstood by incumbents who have spent years perfecting their own playbook to win markets. Even if the pattern is well understood, the incumbent can be disadvantaged: technology often changes where business value is derived from and, in doing so, can reduce the worth of the incumbent's assets at the same time as the market is shifting. It is those very assets, once highly valued and sometimes highly leveraged, that themselves become the proverbial noose around the neck.

Chris Anderson, former editor of *The Economist* and author of *The Long Tail*, hints at some of the changes. In his book, he explains how when distribution costs fall, large incumbents that rely on their power to control distribution are at risk. For example, prior to Google, distribution of information required a different, less scalable infrastructure, and power came from controlling distribution. Whether that distribution was in the form of a newspaper with its physical infrastructure, a network on television, or a large marketing budget that crowded others out, controlling distribution was paramount and expensive. Digital delivery changed the rules. Information could travel much further and faster, and, as a result, it reduced the value of traditional distribution power.

Blockbuster, at the height of its popularity, had more than 84,000 employees and more than 9,000 stores. Its advantage was built around a physical distribution strategy that had its stores located close to customers. It used the power of its scale to have more hits in stock and to negotiate with content producers. But Blockbuster didn't see the rate of technology advancement and consequently failed to see a world where digital delivery was instantaneous and free (or almost free)—a world where consumers wouldn't walk in its doors and plonk down two or three bucks to borrow a video and then pay late fees because they forgot to drive back to the store and return it on time.

It seems easy to see now, but at the time that executives were making these decisions, download speeds made stream-ing impossible and Netflix relied on the physical delivery of DVDs. Unable to grasp how fast technology was moving, it was easy for them to be complacent. By the time they could see what was coming, it was too late. They were playing a game they couldn't win. Blockbuster's main competitive advantage that drove business value for years prior—having 9,000 stores, with the attendant costs—became its disadvan-tage almost overnight. The most innovative thing they could do was add candy aisles to their stores. The extra revenue only delayed the inevitable: revenues went up in the short term, only to fall off the cliff the next year.

Did Blockbuster have bad management? No. They were trapped in existing frameworks. Even if they had known what was coming and could solve it, their existing business model didn't give them any advantage in the new market. The cost to keep the old business going and pivot to a new business would have been extraordinarily high. Netflix created; Blockbuster was destroyed.

I know what it must have looked like from both sides. I've been there: leading a company with a business model that worked for a while, but then realizing that a transition was necessary to preserve the future.

The BuildDirect journey

I cofounded BuildDirect in late 1999 because of a desire to bring more transparency and accountability to building and renovations. With the help of an exceptional team, we were fortunate to make it through some very tough years. It took the belief of some great investors and everything we personally had. At one point, with three children under four years old, my wife agreed to sell our family home and invest all of the proceeds into the business. The business succeeded and was doubling sales each year as an ecommerce company before we blew it up... on purpose.

We were victims of our own success. Customers wanted to buy more from us, but we were failing them because we often didn't have the inventory. We had tried for years to solve this problem but just couldn't keep up with the growth. So at the end of 2013, I went to our board and told them our only way forward was to change almost everything about how we did business. If we didn't, we would stagnate and fail. If we did, we might be able to create something exponentially more valuable.

Our idea was to open our platform—our onboarding of new products, our predictive data about what would sell best, our logistics network for delivery, everything—so our suppliers could understand demand, quickly adjust their inventory accordingly, and give customers what they wanted. In short, we'd get out of the way and put our suppliers in the driver's seat. What was once proprietary, we would give away. Ultimately, this would mean wider selection and better results for the customer.

Pivoting a business as a startup—learning and finding the right product-market fit—is what makes it successful. Pivoting a business that has reached half a billion dollars in market capitalization and is growing quickly is a completely different thing. The very things that make the former business successful slow the transition to the new.

We launched the platform with Home Marketplace in February 2016, and it took off like a rocket—only to fall victim to its own runaway momentum. Suppliers loved the platform and added products to our site faster than we could have imagined. We went from 6,000 products, or SKUs, to more than 150,000 very quickly. But parts of the technology required to handle this growth were still in development. As a result, customers couldn't easily discover the products they needed. Meanwhile, suppliers had great information, but they didn't yet have the tools to adjust their offerings to account for it. We were partway to building the platform we envisioned, but completing it would take a lot more money than anticipated. Terrifyingly, there was no way to turn back.

Elon Musk's famous analysis—"Being an entrepreneur is like eating glass and staring into an abyss"—comes to mind when I think back on those months. The pressure at that point in the journey was horrendous. You lose believers. Investors, suppliers, and members of your team find their firmest convictions pushed to the limit. Some relationships I thought were rock solid crumbled.

People had reason to doubt. Our once-growing revenues had stalled. Suppliers who had been with us for years saw their products buried under the avalanche of new offerings on our site, and customers couldn't easily find the products they needed. It's much harder to hold faith in a grand vision when every new data point warns of disaster.

As this problem intensified, I made a fateful decision to bring more debt into the company to try to get to the other side of our technology build. With that capital infusion in place, we continued to push through. The path was right, but it needed to be finished to provide the value we imagined.

Our suppliers rallied behind us. Great employees dug in, bringing our team together and focusing on solutions under very trying circumstances. We had a lot of people determined to make things work no matter what—and we needed every one of them. Seeing their commitment and passion made me realize that, regardless of the outcome, this was all worthwhile.

Then, as the technology caught up to the demand, things began to coalesce. Revenue started to grow again—this time without the same cost. Incredibly, we were crossing this chasm—together, my whole team and I; we were making it. It was working. After so many years, the dream of creating the simplest and most trusted solution for home improvement was within our sights.

Unfortunately, though, there were new hurdles. Trying to pivot from a legacy business model to a new one takes time, and I felt the weight of old expectations holding us down as we tried to sprint forward. In addition, the partners and debt we took on to finance our technology came with certain realities. Their understanding of growth was different; their timelines for return were different; their appetite for risk was different. In the end, I made the decision to take on debt to fuel our company at a pivotal point in its history. It felt like a last resort at the time. That decision created an unforeseen roadblock in how I led BuildDirect forward, specifically how to maintain our vision and how to protect the investment of staff, investors, and partners who had believed in our company for the better part of eighteen years.

That journey was far more exciting and more terrifying than I could have ever imagined. It was also life-changing. I witnessed first-hand how fast technology is changing the world. I set about to help change an industry, and the job of trying to do that changed me. The entire process forced me to take stock repeatedly, doggedly: What did I value most? How could I ensure a win for the people who believed in the company, even if it meant walking away with nothing? And what would I do if it all went to zero—could I live with that?

In the end, I realized that the things in life I valued most—family, friends, integrity—weren't contingent on business outcomes and couldn't be taken away from me no matter what. Framed that way, all the challenges and risks of running a business were eminently more manageable. In that formulation, the riskiest proposition of all is to lose sight of who I was. To betray myself was the only way to truly fail. And for that reason, I left—with nothing but with everything.

I didn't realize it at the time, but it would turn out to be one of the greatest gifts.

The windows of opportunity

Creative destruction doesn't happen at a steady rate over time. At certain points in history, there is more opportunity for entrepreneurs to create disruption. As Bill Gross, founder and CEO of Idealab, noted, the most overlooked facet of creating a successful enterprise is the role of luck and timing. Too early, and the cost or market doesn't fit; too late, and new monopolies are already forming, making it all but impossible to enter.

I am acutely aware of the role of luck and timing in my own story, as well as those of many of my friends who have both succeeded—or failed—by the narrowest of margins. In 2015, Bill Gross gave a great TED Talk in Vancouver (viewed more than two million times) where he discussed his research on the differences between companies that succeeded or failed. The findings surprised even Bill when he determined that timing stood out above all in determining success rates of startups. In fact, 42 percent of the success could be attributed to timing. Rounding out the top five things in determining success were the team/execution at 32 percent, the idea at 28 percent, the business model at 24 percent, and funding at 14 percent.

Sometimes, the act of creative destruction and the luck in timing is regulatory. China's remarkable rise in the last thirty years serves as a good example. Chinese policy changes that started in 1978 set the stage for a complete reinvention of its economy. As the policies changed, so did the pace of urbanization, as workers were drawn from the countryside to higher-paying jobs in cities. The process of opening markets to capital and trade led to the establishment of China as a major exporter, and entrepreneurs have thrived in creating some of the world's leading companies through this transition, creating enormous wealth for the country and for those entrepreneurs. I specifically think of Jack Ma, the former school teacher who rose from humble beginnings to found Alibaba, one of the world's leading companies. Imagine if, instead of starting in the early 2000s, he had been trying to create his company in the 1970s, with a closed economy in China. Instead of building one of the largest companies of our time, that Jack Ma—with the same entrepreneurial drive and skills— would have likely stayed a school teacher.

Disruption windows also open through breakthroughs in technology. The Industrial Revolution was one such time period. We are in the midst of something even more radical today. In other words, being born in the right moment in time increases your odds of success. This is why perseverance plays such an important role in entrepreneurship. If the windows that open are small, it is more likely that successful entrepreneurs are early, not late, which requires them do whatever it takes to keep their businesses going until the market arrives.

Look at the automotive industry. Henry Ford failed in his first business because the technology required to create the automobile made it too expensive to scale. He started the Detroit Automobile Company in 1899; it failed in late 1901 because the cars were of low quality and high price. But he persevered, and a quickly changing landscape of technology allowed him to find his breakthrough with the Model T and the assembly line. The Model T is credited with bringing inexpensive transportation to a massive scale. That business and its monopoly power helped Ford create other novel ideas that became symbols of innovation, one of which was his ideas around pay and work, which subsequently gave rise to a vibrant middle class.

Ford succeeded because of creativity and perseverance, but also because he had the right timing. Look at the world's largest automotive companies today: many of them started in a fairly narrow window of time when the horse-and-buggy industry was ripe for being destroyed. In the US, Ford was founded in 1903 and General Motors in 1908; in Germany, BMW in 1916 and Daimler-Benz in 1926; in Sweden, Volvo in 1927; in Japan, Nissan in 1933, Toyota in 1937, and Honda in 1948. Out of the thousands of other car companies that were started, most merged or failed.

And then the window closed. Even a visionary leader such as John DeLorean, an industry maverick who is credited with the first muscle car while at GM, who quickly rose through the ranks as the youngest GM of Chevrolet, failed miserably when he stepped out and competed against such monopoly power with his DeLorean Motor Company.

Many of those same automotive giants, after thriving for more than 100 years, may fall in the years ahead because of a radically changing landscape of technology around self-driving and electric cars.

Forecasting the timing of change and taking advantage of it may be the most important skillsets of a visionary entre-preneur. Why, then, is it so rare for previous winners to stay winners? They obviously had the skillset to grow monopolies and thrive. Do they get caught in what made them success-ful in the past, keeping them from evolving in the changing landscape?

For many companies, that is an important question today due to an incredibly fast-changing environment that will make it ever more difficult to compete using past successes as any guide to the future.

Most people will forget that even Jeff Bezos, founder and CEO of Amazon and one of the great visionaries and opera-tors of our time, was at one time precipitously close to the edge of disaster and criticized widely for the very things that would make his company so successful and celebrated today. In 2001, Amazon had lost about 94 percent of its market value from its peak in 1999, and the analysts were all over it, with some saying that it would not survive. One such ana-lyst, Ravi Suria from Lehman Brothers, wrote the following blistering report:

From a bond perspective, we find the credit extremely weak and deteriorating... The company's inability to make hard cash per unit sold is clearly manifested in the weak balance sheet, poor working capital management, and massive negative operating cash flow—the financial characteristics that have driven innumerable retailers to disaster throughout history... Adding to the operational weakness is the mounting pile of debt, as Amazon has essentially funded its revenues through a variety of sources over the past year. From 1997 through the last quarter, the company has received $2.8 billion in funding, while its revenues have been $2.9 billion—a whopping $0.95 for every dollar of merchandise sold... In its current situation of high debt load, high interest costs, spiraling inventory, and rising expansion costs, we believe that current cash balances will last the company through the first quarter of 2001 under the best-case scenario... the company will run out of cash within the next four quarters unless it manages to pull a financing rabbit out of its rather magical hat.[10]

Today, this analysis looks outright crazy. Amazon's reach is staggering. It controls a business that accounts for almost 8 percent of all US retail sales, and 45 cents of every dollar sold online. All other retailers combined—including Walmart, Home Depot, Target, eBay, Best Buy, and Costco—fight over the remaining 55 cents sold online. It has 199 million monthly unique users on its sites and 100 million Prime members that pay an annual fee to Amazon for special deals.[11] Besides selling products and services, Amazon also leverages the technology it builds by allowing others to access it for their businesses. Amazon Web Services is an $80 billion business on its own and controls 32 percent of cloud computing.

Somewhat ironically, it was Lehman Brothers that failed to see what was coming in the credit crisis of 2008 and was forced into bankruptcy.

Beyond the smarts, drive, and curiosity of Bezos, it's easy to see that without a little luck and timing, it all could have been different. It's interesting to stop for a moment and imagine how different the stories would be about Bezos's vision or Amazon's operations management had it gone the other way—which it just as easily could have.

The pattern of creative destruction and monopoly power stands out when we look at the list of the top companies in the world only ten years ago compared to today. Ten years ago, many of the top companies in the world were started in the late 1800s. Today, the list is dominated by technology platforms taking advantage of network effects and data capture to enhance their services.

This is an important time. Incredible opportunities still abound, as shifts in technology make it easier to consolidate information and create new platforms in industries where they don't yet exist. But the large platforms realize it, too: they have hundreds of millions of people who use their services every day, they understand what is different about their models in ways few people do, and they already have monopoly power. Competing with them for platform-type power, even in a new market and a fast-changing environment, will take more than a little luck and timing. For non-technology companies, it will be even more difficult if you're using past successes as the guide to the future.

Largest Companies in 2019 versus in 2009

2019				2009			
Rank	Company	Country	usbn$	Rank	Company	Country	usbn$
1	Apple	US	1,099	1	Petro-China	China	390
2	Microsoft	US	1,056	2	Exxon-Mobil	US	345
3	Alphabet (Google's parent company)	US	873	3	Industrial & Commercial Bank of China	China	250
4	Amazon	US	872	4	China Mobile	China	210
5	Facebook	US	531	5	Microsoft	US	205
6	Berkshire Hathaway	US	517	6	Walmart	US	198
7	Alibaba	China	442	7	China Construction Bank	China	195
8	JPMorgan Chase	US	400	8	Johnson & Johnson	US	172
9	Visa	US	372	9	Procter & Gamble	US	170
10	Johnson & Johnson	US	343	10	Royal Dutch Shell	UK & Netherlands	169

It's an even bigger issue than it appears. The major platforms control much more than you might be aware of. Because they control the highways and commons of technology, they have asymmetric power over all other types of companies. They are also the ones at the forefront of creating artificial intelligence (AI), which could very well make them the most powerful and important companies to have ever existed.

If a superintelligence is created by a commercial company or small number of companies, the value will accrue to mostly them. If this happens, it would be hard to see the entrepreneurial process continuing in the same way that it has in the past. In an environment where a company controlled AI, wouldn't that AI itself consolidate power quickly? How could we reasonably expect an entrepreneur without that same access to compete against a superintelligence? If you are at least partially convinced that luck and timing have as much to do with success as anything else, then, by logical conclusion, this time window may be the luckiest of all—with all the times that follow this window being unlucky. And that, too, would have dire consequences for the way our economic systems are built. A major structural reform would be needed to keep the entrepreneurial process moving forward.

The rise of the platforms

The new super monopolies, including Google, Apple, Amazon, Alibaba, and Tencent, have been created by understanding the ways in which the world has changed—where the power is held has changed and the former monopolies find it hard to compete in those spaces. Not only that, because of the immense value they bring to their users—their platforms are designed to take advantage of network effects and the data that it brings them—these monopolies are likely to continue to consolidate power.

Strong network effects are at the core of every platform business today. In fact, in a recent three-year study by NFX, network effects accounted for 70 percent of the value in technology companies over the last twenty-three years.[12] Network effects are very different from the economies of scale which traditionally drove power. Through economies of scale, the bigger a company was, the more buying power and leverage it had to squeeze out competitors. In contrast, a network effect exists when the value of a product or service gives more value to each user as the number of users increases. A telephone system is a good example: if I am the only one with a phone, the service is useless because I cannot call anyone. With each additional user, the service becomes more valuable to all users, which in turn creates a positive feedback loop of value leading to exponential growth.

Designing a platform to take advantage of strong network effects creates lock-in and winner-take-all markets. The Internet itself has one of the strongest network effects, and consequently so do many of the top companies built on it. Ironically, network effects, which were supposed to make the Internet the great equalizer as it redistributed power away from monopolies, have ended up concentrating even more power in the hands of very few.

Beyond network effects, every consumer platform gains its power in a similar way. Most people falsely believe that the majority of power is gained through consumers of the platform. That is only partly correct and is largely a consequence of what the platform's core focus is really on. The value they offer consumers is extraordinary, which drives consumers at an increasing rate, but the secret common to all of them is that they derive the value they give consumers by their focus on aggregating supply. Not just some of the supply, either, but all of it.

Aggregating all supply and allowing that supply to compete for audiences is how all platforms gain their power. That supply can take many different forms, but the pattern is remarkably consistent. On Facebook, the supply is you. On LinkedIn, the supply is the business you. On Amazon and Alibaba, the supply is the products and suppliers. On YouTube, it is the videos. On Airbnb, it is the rental homes. On iTunes or Spotify, it is the songs and musicians. In an app store, it is the apps. In any one of these examples, imagine the service without the sheer number of "suppliers" competing for attention. Because the platform owners don't own the supply, they aggregate it, the supply can scale almost indefinitely without the negative impacts of holding that supply. Few buyers realize the vastness of the supply side because they only "see" the top results, and the top results are constantly being tailored for them to drive conversion higher. Amazon has more than 500 million products vying for your attention, with teams trying to optimize their products to stay on top. Google now indexes more than 130 trillion individual web pages.[13] Each of those pages belongs to a site, and every commercial site has a team behind it doing what they can to rise to the top of the search rankings.

For users on the platforms, the obvious primary benefit is more choice and unique content or products. They don't need to go anywhere else. The secondary effect is more important: it creates competition, which drives the suppliers to compete for users' attention. This competition enables a better buyer experience because the highest converting products or services naturally rise to the top. The competition also provides vast and differentiated data to apply machine learning. The machine learning, in turn, continues to drive a better buyer experience by identifying the best product or service for each customer out of its vast supply.

Imagine if Google had the same content as the Yellow Pages, or if YouTube had the same content as your local cable station. There would be less value to users, and less reason to go to either. YouTube doesn't create the vast majority of the content it hosts: it offers a place to aggregate it and therefore all of the cost is in the content providers' hands to create videos that stand out, while YouTube's benefit to its users increases as it aggregates more content. At last count, more than 576,000 hours of video are created on YouTube every day of the week. And once it's there, it's available at any time (unless it's deliberately removed, of course). That's a lot of opportunity to match almost infinite supply to demand.

Imagine if Airbnb competed the same way as hotels do, with a limited supply of rooms. If Airbnb had a selection of ten rooms in New York to compete with a hotel you normally choose, the hotel would win every time. But the game changes when Airbnb aggregates far more supply on their platform. At a certain tipping point, the service locks in and provides immense value to users through access to a unique supply that they hadn't seen before; the suppliers, in this case, make their listings stand out by various means like better photos or feedback scores that, in turn, deliver increasing value to users. And, like YouTube, not only does Airbnb have no cost of the supply beyond their technology, the value they gain is from the competition of the supply. Today, Airbnb has more than six million listings.

Because of this pattern, for users, platforms are incredible and getting better all the time. It is no wonder that we are locked into them. For suppliers, however, it can be more difficult—especially if you're late to a platform.

Legacy Suppliers versus Tech Disrupters

Product/service	Legacy (choice made by people, distorts true picture)	Disrupter (enables all choice)	Supply number of disrupter
Music	Sony Music BMG	iTunes	30 million songs
Books as key beachhead and expanding to all	Barnes & Noble Chapters	Amazon	+500 million SKUs (166 million in fashion and beauty)
Accommodation	Four Seasons Holiday Inn Hilton	Airbnb	+6 million
Search/media	WarnerMedia Yellow Pages Newspapers	Google YouTube	+133 trillion

Being early on a platform can yield terrific results for supply. A hack I used on Twitter gives a good example. Realizing
the pattern—that supply was needed for the platform owners
and being early mattered—I decided to write a blog post in
early 2008 titled "Why Every CEO Needs to Be on Twitter."
In this case, I was a supplier (a CEO) that validated the platform for other CEOs. Two days later, something extraordinary
happened: after using the service for months before that with
limited interactions, my Twitter account exploded—gaining
over 1,000 followers a day. It took some time to figure out
what had happened. Then a friend sent me a screenshot of
his Twitter onboarding process: there was a list of ten CEOs
that every new Twitter member should follow. There I was—
the only one of the ten that didn't belong on the list. Right
between Richard Branson and Bill Gates. As I gained more
followers, the rate increased as my number of followers itself
convinced others I was worth following. That one blog post
and the subsequent actions by Twitter drove my followers to
more than 185,000 almost overnight.

That example shows that standing out early on a platform
can yield impressive results, creating broad distribution and
reach where there was none before. Those early successes
are very real, with much of the value accruing to the supplier.
New stars are created, whether they are gamers, Instagram or
Twitter celebrities, Airbnb listings, or products. Those stars in
turn encourage more suppliers who see that success and want
to duplicate it. With that competition, the platform starts to
gain more leverage in pricing power over the suppliers and
each supplier is forced to work harder to keep up.

As a supplier on the platform, the analogy that comes to mind is picking up $100 bills while a steamroller is coming towards you. I'll use Google as an example, but the pattern can be applied to almost every platform. When Google and ecommerce were still relatively new, winning "organic" or free search was almost like winning the lottery. And because there was relatively little competition, it didn't take much to "win" the top spots in their search algorithm. For my business and many others that were early, it felt like picking up $100 bills—and we didn't know a steamroller was coming. The business grew quickly because our "advertising" cost was essentially free. Our "supply" of content to Google was a star. As more companies realized this power, our competitors raced in, trying to win the coveted top spots as well, which made winning them harder for us. (It also made the consumer experience better!) The steamroller was now moving towards us and we needed to move as well—to where there were only $20 bills to pick up. We remembered what picking up $100 bills looked like, and we wanted that back, so we expanded our team to compete and create better content. All of this competition was at our cost to win Google. Competitors continued to race in for the terms we wanted, constantly increasing our cost to win and at the same time reducing our chances to win.

To see how unlikely it is to win a top spot today, we'll use an example of a search on hardwood flooring. "Hardwood flooring" today brings up 1.25 billion results on Google. That's a lot of teams and a lot of money fighting for limited prime real estate on Google—a top-of-the-first-page search result.

Google gives us the illusion of choice. How many times have you, as a Google user, ever gone to page 35,000? With this, we see the fallacy. We can have all of the choice we want, if we look for long enough, but because of our limited time, we trust what Google puts at the top of the results and rarely go to even the second page.

And so our company was doing more and more and getting less and less—unable to get off the wheel, having relied on it as our primary channel. Then, just as all hope was lost, we were given a golden opportunity: our business could pay 5 cents per click to Google and have our results listed above all the organic listings. It didn't matter that we still had a team of people working to win organic, and that organic listings were now less valuable because they were pushed down in the search results by the paid results. As with the pattern before on organic search, early on, paying for top spots worked really well. But the pattern then repeated itself, now on paid results, as competitors raced in. The 5 cents rose to over $5.00. Through the journey, I also realized that in a competitive world, there is always a company that will pay more than what is economically reasonable to "win the market." One day, with an enormous cost and deteriorating returns, the steamroller will run over you.

The overall dynamic is why most platforms are monopoly businesses. Early on, the potential results are too impressive for supply to overlook the opportunity. Later, all the buyers are already there so there is almost no choice but to get involved. The network effect of the platform creates a world where the "cost" to suppliers to get buyers' attention constantly increases but in doing so drives lower cost or higher value to buyers.

In the past, monopolies were often broken up because of their negative effects on consumers in the form of increased pricing or constraining markets. The monopolies today are constructed differently and do the exact opposite for consumers. The consumers win in the form of better pricing and service—which is deflationary—and, therefore, the monopolies are hard to stop. As I learned the hard way, you are either the platform or the arbitrage on the platform. In the long term, there is no in-between.

On the eve of destruction

It is somewhat ironic that Schumpeter's term creative destruction is so widely used in capitalism to celebrate the process of innovation. Schumpeter himself was pessimistic about the long-term sustainability of the process. He saw it as ultimately leading to the undermining of capitalism's own institutional frameworks. In his own words, "In breaking down the pre-capitalist framework of society, capitalism thus broke not only barriers that impeded its progress but also flying buttresses that prevented its collapse. The capitalist process in much the same way in which it destroyed the institutional framework of feudal society also undermines its own."[14]

Schumpeter's view is consistent with that of Nobel laureate Hyman Minsky, but not in the way you might think.

Minsky, an American economist, theorized that long periods of financial stability naturally lead to instability because of the rise of debt. The "Minsky moment" is the tipping point where the debt-fuelled asset bubble collapses, assets become difficult to sell at any price, and a market collapse ensues. Interestingly, though, Minsky didn't forecast a write-down in debt. Although Minsky, who passed away in 1996, is legendary for the Minsky moment, his most prominent call was something else. Minsky realized that even governments that preached free-market rules, when faced with a systematic collapse, would always act as the lender of last resort and bail out the market. In effect, he believed they would be forced to do so because not doing so would cause too much short-term pain. In his 1986 book, *Stabilizing an Unstable Economy*, Minsky wrote, "Every time the Federal Reserve protects a financial instrument, it legitimizes the use of this instrument to finance activity. This means that not only does Federal Reserve action abort an incipient crisis, but it sets the stage for a resumption in the process of increasing indebtedness—and makes possible the introduction of new instruments."[15]

This is where I believe Minsky and Schumpeter converge. It is not the debt itself that acts to undermine capitalism. It is the act of stabilizing an economy through socializing the losses when faced with a collapse that undermines capitalism's own institutional framework.

So, instead of writing down debt in the global financial crisis of 2008, the world's debt load has grown almost 50 percent higher, now more than three times as large as the global economy. And if stimulus is removed from markets, we can expect things to break down and collapse quickly. If Minsky is correct, we should therefore expect more easing, and more chaos from it, as the can is kicked down the road once again.

As Nassim Nicholas Taleb cleverly points out in his book *Antifragile*, "Small forest fires periodically cleanse the system of the most flammable material, so this does not have the opportunity to accumulate. Systematically preventing forest fires from taking place 'to be safe' makes the big one much worse."[16] By continuing to add debt and kick the can down the road, governments and central banks have prevented some of the small fires—in this case, the pain of restructuring. I realize that calling the 2008 crisis and the monetary easing that allowed the economies of the world to escape restructuring a "small fire" is akin to calling the Great Depression a "recession." The problem, though, is that in choosing that option, the size of the fire on the horizon is unimaginable.

Monopolies that have flourished for a long time are often overturned very quickly because they fail to recognize an impending transition. Tipping points can come from anywhere and can come quite suddenly, often with little warning of the cascading effects. But what happens when, instead of the monopoly being a business or a small part of an overall economy, the monopoly is our entire interconnected economic system? Our way of making money and our inflationary bias? Put the lagging GDP growth with illusionary asset inflation, plus an impossible-to-maintain rise of debt, against a backdrop of technology growing at an exponential rate, and the phase transition starts to come into focus.

We will need a whole new way of seeing things and perhaps a whole new way of living. What is coming next in technology changes the rules in a way that too few understand.

3

IT IS HARD TO
THINK DIFFERENTLY

W E OFTEN LOOK at previous generations or to other areas of the world and see examples of thinking that we find almost impossible to believe with our current knowledge. Our history is filled with long-held beliefs that governed the way people lived... until those beliefs were changed.

Only 400 years ago, Galileo Galilei enraged the Church by suggesting that the Earth might not be the centre of the universe. If true, the change would break some of the underlying pillars of the Church's teachings and subsequent power. To populations without telescopes, it was equally hard to accept: it didn't match their everyday ground-level view of reality. Between 1450 and 1750, hysteria about witches ebbed and flowed in society and led to thousands of executions. Events like the spread of disease were attributed to witchcraft when the true source was hidden from view.

And, of course, we did not all become suddenly enlightened in the eighteenth or nineteenth centuries. It wasn't until August 1920 that the 19th Amendment to the US Constitution finally granted equal voting rights to women in America. For almost 100 years prior, women's rights leaders like Susan B. Anthony and Elizabeth Cady Stanton had been arguing tirelessly that women should have the same rights as men. Anthony was arrested for voting in 1872. Their position seems obvious to us now, but in 1911 J.B. Sanford, senator, chairman of Democratic Caucus, gave voice to a prevailing belief of the time: "The mother's influence is needed in the home. She can do little good by gadding the streets and neglecting her children. Woman is woman. She cannot unsex herself or change her sphere. Let her be content with her lot and perform those high duties intended for her by the Great Creator, and she will accomplish far more in governmental affairs that she can ever accomplish by mixing up in the dirty pool of politics."[17]

Today, we look at such pieces of history and think of ourselves as enlightened, forgetting that it was not long ago when the majority of the population—both men and women—fought against it. We find it difficult to believe that some other societies reject and fight against these beliefs in the same way as our ancestors did. But we're thinking with the same brains that humans have always had, and we still have long-held beliefs and biases. It turns out that beliefs are hard to change, even when the facts are on your side. Entire populations make up stories that guide their actions without realizing that much of it is a figment of their imaginations and has little to do with facts.

How many of our own beliefs stand up to facts? To future generations, how many of our current actions fuelled by those beliefs will look outright foolish? Will the economic dogma of today—that growth is always good, no matter how much you change the rules to get it—look as irrational to historians of tomorrow as geocentric cosmology, the burning of witches, or voter inequality are to us today?

Building on weak foundations

Our minds accept patterns that match our sense of reality and discard other patterns that we are not familiar with. We rely on simple frameworks or mental models so our brains' limited energy can be directed into what we deem most important and don't get bogged down in questioning things that we already know.

Think of all the things that you do on autopilot: you wake up, shower, brush your teeth, get dressed, have breakfast, and drive to the office, all without much active thinking required. Now imagine that you had to learn every one of those activities like it was your first time. If you had to consciously think through every task again and again, you would be exhausted before you left the house. The ability to learn and assimilate information frees up your brain to think about more important things.

Deep thinking and learning is also taxing on our energy stores, and so we require simplification and reinforcement. Our minds, through repetition or emotion, learn things and then, having committed them to memory, rely on this information and often never question it again; we put our energy into other things we deem more important. Like building a structure with a strong base, we make our mental models the foundation for adding newer information. We notice things that match our view and we dismiss things that do not. As we build our narrow knowledge on top of that foundation, we might not even realize when the foundation itself is weak.

And so, as we go on with our lives, filtering a massive amount of information, we can easily become blind to important information, caught in our own bubbles, disregarding some information or alternative views, even when it might be helpful to us. Our decisions are shaped by what we regard as the facts, and if new information emerges that belies what we believe, it often hardens us to our original view.

It also means that we can often only see what is right in front of us without seeing the larger forces that shape our lives.

As we saw with the 2008 financial meltdown, even top experts may not see big changes coming because they, too, are human beings with the same cognitive biases as all of us, thinking along established paths. The longer any pattern persists, the more comfortable the experts become in explaining the pattern and reinforcing their views, preventing them from seeing things a beginner's mind might readily see. After all, in long periods of stability, most of the alternative views prove false and the experts are often right in dismissing them. But in times of great change, the beginner's mind has the advantage. Without the same fortified foundation of knowledge, the beginner's mind asks *why* with the intent to discover the answer and not to defend a previous reality. It is one of the main drivers of the creative destruction process. The expert's position is one of the key factors to be creatively destroyed.

George Eastman invented the Kodak Black camera in 1888 with a goal "to make the camera as convenient as a pencil." By 1907 the company had more than 5,000 employees, and for over 100 years, they dominated the photography industry. In 1976, Kodak held 90 percent of film sales and 85 percent of camera sales in the United States. At its peak in 1996, it had over two-thirds of the global market, with sales of $16 billion and a company value of over $31 billion. The downfall of Kodak was incredible because a Kodak employee, Steve Sasson, actually invented the first digital camera in 1975 and the first DSLR camera in 1989. Both times, he pitched executives who failed to see how the digital camera would shape the future of the industry. They were so caught up in their framework of protecting "film" sales; it is easy to see why. And so after thriving for more than 130 years, Kodak filed for bankruptcy in 2012.

Sears actually invented the mail-order catalogue business in 1892. Before that, consumers had limited access to mass-produced goods. By increasing the selection of products and shipping them to homes, Sears, Roebuck and Company grew quickly and its catalogue became iconic. It opened its first physical store in 1927, and up until Walmart surpassed it in the early 1990s, Sears was the largest retailer in the United States. In 2018, Sears filed for bankruptcy. And yet Sears's original business was based on the same principle that Amazon's is today: greater choice delivered to your home.

It doesn't just happen in business. It happens to all of us and it happens much more often than we might believe. Trapped in our own sense of reality, we often hold onto false beliefs. Despite how certain we feel, our own views are not always right.

Two-speed thinking

Nobel laureate, psychologist, and author Daniel Kahneman sheds some light on the cognitive biases that can lead us to flawed thinking and reasoning. In one of my favourite books, *Thinking, Fast and Slow*, Kahneman describes the two systems we use for thinking: system 1 is fast—quick decisions based on our intuition and influenced by emotions. System 2 is slower, more deliberate, and thought out—and, not surprisingly, not as prone to mistakes as our quick response system.

When we use system 1, we're quick to rely on the narrative we believe, however flawed and not backed up by verifiable evidence it may be. We have cognitive biases that hardwire us to fool ourselves, and even those with a deep understanding of cognitive biases can be fooled. Kahneman explains, "As we navigate our lives, we normally allow ourselves to be guided by impressions and feelings, and the confidence we have in our intuitive beliefs and preferences is usually justified. But not always. We are often confident even when we are wrong, and an objective observer is more likely to detect our errors than we are."[18]

Let's look at a couple of examples from our everyday lives: the anchoring effect and the sunk-cost bias.

The anchoring effect happens when our minds put too much weight on initial information when making decisions. All subsequent judgments are then made in relation to this anchor. If you need to borrow $1,000 from a friend, it is much easier to first ask for $5,000 and then say that you actually only need $1,000 than it is to ask for $500 and then increase it to $1,000. Even though the final request is the same, the later number is compared against the initial anchor in each case and it feels better when going from the large to the small in this case. This cognitive bias fools us often: in negotiations, where someone sets the initial anchor high, with sale prices, and even in our relationships.

Sunk-cost bias happens when you continue to invest time or money into something because of the time or emotion you have already put in. As Kahneman points out, the potential of losses is a much more powerful motivator than potential for gains. When someone stays in a bad relationship, investment, or job, they are often unknowingly a victim of the sunk-cost bias, keeping in the status quo for fear of change, even though the status quo is something that they do not want. It doesn't just happen to individuals; it happens in systems, too. I personally believe that the sunk-cost bias is making us hold onto an economic system that is clearly failing for fear of loss of the status quo.

These are just two of the 150 or so known cognitive biases. Additional biases such as confirmation bias—where we search for information that confirms our perceptions—and bias blind spot—when we recognize a bias in others' decision-making while failing to see it in ourselves—mean we are often not as clever as we believe. Patterns reinforce themselves and we do not see that we have trapped ourselves in our own boxes. But these boxes are easier to see in others, which leaves a door open for creative destruction.

This is why Amazon is valued almost three times as high as Walmart, once the most valuable company in the world. Walmart became the king of retail by relentlessly driving better selection and value for consumers. The executive teams were filled with some of the smartest people around... locked into a box of their own creation, defending it while failing to see that it had become what was hurting their value.

A store—even a large one—is constrained by shelf space. Even the biggest stores have an upper limit of 130,000 products. When there are high costs to your stores and limits to your shelves, you must pick only the bestselling products. To pick the best products, you must hire merchandisers to wade through the vast supply. The gatekeepers of the products, the choosers, believe that they are really good at the job because of the self-reinforcing mechanism of the demand in their stores: consumers can't choose what they don't see. But every product that is not chosen at Walmart is still also looking for consumers. Amazon fills this need with its effectively endless shelf space: 500 million products rather than 130,000. It doesn't staff choosers in the same way because the shoppers do the choosing as the suppliers do the promoting. Constrained by the boxes of their big but not limitless stores, Walmart executives couldn't see that they were being beaten on very thing that Walmart relied on: greater choice and superior pricing. Even if you include Walmart's online selection in its total number of products, Walmart still has less than 5 percent of Amazon's products.

As Jeff Bezos said in 2019, "I very frequently get the question: 'What's going to change in the next ten years?' And that is a very interesting question; it's a very common one. I almost never get the question: 'What's not going to change in the next ten years?' And I submit to you that that second question is actually the more important of the two—because you can build a business strategy around the things that are stable in time... In our retail business, we know that customers want low prices, and I know that's going to be true ten years from now. They want fast delivery; they want vast selection."[19]

Will something replace Amazon's monopoly? There is a chance that Amazon or the others racing to create artificial intelligence will gain a lock-in that we underestimate, in turn driving asymmetric benefits to the platforms that would be almost impossible to break. But technology isn't slowing down. Besides artificial intelligence, a wave of disruption like 3D printing could change where value is derived from again and provide an opening for a new company to invent everything anew.

Instead of simply believing that you would be better at facing the disruption than Walmart has been—or Blockbuster, or Kodak, or Sears—imagine if you were in their shoes. Imagine it was your business and what you would do when most of the profits still come from stores, but the future is in digital. In fact, you *are* in their shoes—maybe not in business, but that same disruptive force is happening to you and everything around you. And as easy as it is to read examples such as these and say that we wouldn't get trapped, the evidence says otherwise. We are all human, and we all have cognitive biases that make it difficult to see important changes.

But there's even more to it. Beyond our biases and entrenched thinking, we have entire narratives that we expect things to follow.

Myths we live by

Years ago, I watched an interview with Mark Burnett, executive producer of the show *Survivor*, where he credited a professor of literature for his help in creating a winning formula for a show. That professor was Joseph Campbell, author of the 1949 book *The Hero with a Thousand Faces*. Burnett talked about the impact of that book and Campbell's ideas on not just *Survivor* but many of our favourite stories. I was intrigued and wanted to learn more. I was surprised to discover that George Lucas, Bob Dylan, and many other great storytellers of our time also acknowledged the influence of Campbell's work on their own.

Campbell's theory is based on his observation of a common pattern behind the elements of most stories, regardless of their origin. It is found in all mythologies and religions. He calls it "the Hero's Journey" or "monomyth." We see it everywhere, and we *expect* to see it everywhere.

It involves a hero who goes on an adventure, faces almost insurmountable obstacles, wins a victory, and then comes home transformed. It has seventeen stages that can be characterized a number of ways but generally follow three main sections:

1. The Departure—Where the hero of the story lives in a normal world and receives a call for adventure. The hero is typically reluctant to follow the call but is then helped by a mentor.
2. The Initiation—Where the hero faces much adversity and ordeal, eventually reaching the main obstacle or central crisis of his adventure. Then in overcoming it, the hero gains an unexpected treasure.
3. The Return—Where the hero returns to the ordinary world where the treasure can be used for the benefit of his community. The hero himself is transformed by the entire adventure as he gains newfound wisdom—which is the unexpected gift.

Many of humanity's stories fit a narrative that generally follows the Hero's Journey. Without the hero or the struggle, there is no story. The story travels well because it is something that we can all relate to in our own lives of struggle, learning, success, and failure. We see the hero in ourselves and root for them. In that connection, it becomes a story that we remember and pass on. It is easy to understand why this type of storyline is so compelling. Before the ability to mass record our knowledge, simple, compelling narratives were the only way to transmit our knowledge to the next generation.

You can see the Campbell framework everywhere. The brilliant 1997 "Think Different" marketing campaign for Apple celebrates the Hero's Journey:

> Here's to the crazy ones. The misfits. The rebels. The troublemakers. The round pegs in the square holes. The ones who see things differently. They're not fond of rules. And they have no respect for the status quo. You can quote them, disagree with them, glorify or vilify them. About the only thing you can't do is ignore them. Because they change things... They push the human race forward... While some may see them as the crazy ones, we see genius. Because the people who are crazy enough to think they can change the world are the ones who do.

These stories we create are important because they allow us to make sense of the world around us by infusing a narrative with emotion. Emotion is what makes our stories memorable. The more emotion in a story, the stickier it is. We are constantly creating and using stories to explain how the world works and how we fit within it. The stories we choose tend to reinforce our beliefs, from religion, to politics, to good versus evil, to capitalism or socialism or anything else we believe in. An easy-to-follow story arc allows us to simplify the complexity in the world. These simple narratives reinforce not only how we see the world, but also how we think about ourselves.

The problem, though, is that because we don't question our own stories or beliefs very often, we are bound to continue to believe in something even when it makes no logical sense. Worse, because these stories are so powerful in our minds, we can use those simple narratives to define others as villains, whether they belong to a different religious group, company, or other. We will come back to this in greater detail later in the book.

The hero of the story of creative destruction is the entrepreneur. The entrepreneurial journey—such as my own story in starting and leading BuildDirect—fits the same story arc. The entrepreneur finds their calling but faces almost insurmountable odds while doing so; the adventure is difficult, and hard lessons are learned, often changing the entrepreneur. For the story to make sense, though, there needs to be an obstacle to overcome—the bigger the better, whether that obstacle is a villain or otherwise.

And sometimes, faced with a challenge but unwilling to deal with the real problem, we create a false villain and project the struggle on them. Instead of accepting the changes to our life we need to make to deal with a new world reality, for instance, we may decide some group of "others" are at fault and cast ourselves as "heroes" in a narrative against them. It's happened before. It's happening again, as we will see.

How do we overcome our errors?

With all of these narratives and biases making up our mental operating system, how can we tell if there are errors? Especially in a time when there is ever more information competing for our attention, attempting to influence our thoughts and actions? Even if we accept that we are prone to errors in judgment, how do we know when to dig deeper? When might our own views not be built on stable foundations?

Fortunately, there are a number of ways. Avid readers and learners, especially those who study across various fields, will tell you that they read diverse topics so they can connect patterns across disciplines or industries. From this practice, they train their brain to recognize opportunity, seeing what worked in one place and applying it elsewhere. By doing so, these people force themselves to break out of the walls that could trap them and to remain open to possibility.

Another way of error correcting for these natural biases and stories, according to my friend Bob Sutton, is to argue as if you were right, but listen as if you were wrong. Bob is a Stanford professor and bestselling author of *The No Asshole Rule*, and for decades he has studied what makes great leaders. The best leaders are constantly learning, curious about where they made mistakes and actively looking for areas where they might have it wrong. Arguing as if you're right and listening like you're wrong allows leaders to confidently go forward with a direction, while also being able to course correct when new information arises that suggests a better path. Bob's research suggests that not only does it allow for faster learning, but by using similar frameworks, leaders inspire confidence in teams to contribute new ideas and challenge the status quo. Instead of leadership having their heads in the sand, the best ideas win.

This mirrors the approach developed and taught by Paul Saffro, at Palo Alto's Institute for the Future, to thrive in a world where the future is uncertain. The institute teaches "strong opinions, weakly held." Strong opinions allow leaders to move forward quickly, which is important because it avoids information and choice overload. "Weakly held" adds the humility to constantly be learning and ready to course correct. It allows leadership to move past confirmation biases.

This combination of bold moves followed by constant reflection allows for a learning and feedback cycle, which ultimately allows leaders and their companies to error correct at a faster rate than would otherwise be possible. The process is used by the best leaders in business, and beyond business, the same thread exists in the people we consider the wisest among us. Their wisdom comes from an increased learning rate with commitment to feedback from anywhere or anyone.

We will need all the wisdom that we can get to enable our societies to thrive in a world where technology is quickly moving beyond what most can even imagine.

4

THE
TECHNOLOGY BOOM

W HEN I WAS twelve years old, I wanted to be famously rich. I would often joke with my parents about whether I would let them onto my future estate or have them stopped at the moat. (I've learned a lot since.) At dinner one night, my parents asked me to consider which I would rather have—just hypothetically, of course: a million dollars on the spot or a penny that doubles every day for thirty-one days. I made the same mistake that nearly all of us make. I couldn't imagine that a small thing like a penny doubling over time could become so large.

In fact, in just thirty-one days that single penny doubling would become $10,737,418.24. What stood out even more than the dollar amount, though—especially to a twelve-year-old who thought he knew everything—was just how wrong I was. I was sure I would not make this mistake again.

A few years later, one of my teachers told us a story of how chess was invented in India. The ruler of India was so pleased with the game that he asked the inventor of chess to name his reward. The inventor asked for a single grain of rice on the first square of the chess board and then two on the second one and four on the third one, doubling on each subsequent square of the chess board. The ruler, amazed at such a small price, immediately agreed. About two weeks later, the ruler—having found that he had been fooled and the number had grown to more rice than was available in his land—had the inventor executed.

After having missed one exponential pattern by a large amount when my parents gave me a choice on the penny, I was sure I would be able to intuitively understand the pattern when I saw it the next time. But once more, like the penny doubling, I was fooled. As my teacher revealed the final tally of 18,446,744,073,709,551,615 grains of rice, I was blown away by how big the number was. At 0.029 grams per grain of rice, that equals over half a trillion tonnes. Total world rice production today is approximately half a billion tonnes, so that's a thousand years of rice supply at current rates.

Think you've got the pattern now? Imagine If I fold a piece of paper on itself fifty times. (I can only fold it seven times before it resists too much, but let's assume for the moment that I can keep folding it up to fifty times.) How thick would the piece of paper be on fold fifty?

I have asked this question to tens of thousands of people. Most often I get an answer of about two inches, and rarely do I get an answer higher than the ceiling unless someone has heard the answer before. It seems that I'm not alone in my inability to intuitively understand exponential growth. Even though I have now primed your brain to think bigger, before reading on, please take a guess.

The answer is that piece of paper on fold fifty would stretch from the Earth to the sun: 149 million kilometres.

Doubling up

Most people are generally aware of Moore's law. Gordon Moore, cofounder of Intel, described what we now call Moore's law in a 1965 article in *Electronics* magazine. He observed that the number of transistors on a printed circuit board doubled every year and would for at least the next ten years. He later extended that prediction and revised it, saying that doubling would continue every two years. As Moore's law has progressed over the past fifty years, the actual doubling has occurred approximately every eighteen months. Beyond just the doubling of computing power, we should expect a 21 percent annual decline in price to performance.[20]

This combination sets up remarkable gains. For example, according to *Computerworld* magazine, the cost of one megabyte of hard drive memory has fallen from approximately $1 million in 1967 to 2 cents today.[21]

To compare Moore's law with the illustration of folding a piece of paper to the sun, there have been approximately thirty-three doubles of transistors on a circuit board. The paper, after thirty-three folds, would be about 1,136 kilometres thick—that's about the distance from Boston to Detroit, which is far, but nowhere near the sun. In the early folds of the paper—for instance, when you've folded it seven times and it's still less than an inch thick—it is hard to see how it is possible that on fold fifty, a thin piece of paper could reach the sun.

It is the same with technology: as it advances beyond the initial doubles, it's difficult to imagine what is possible with each double. But here is why that is important. All the advances we see around us today are due to the past doubles. And in eighteen months, compute power will double again, and with that, double all of what we have had in the last fifty years. Eighteen months to two years after that, it will double again. Instead of taking little steps on our way to the sun, we are now taking massive leaps. Technology isn't just speeding up; information isn't just speeding up: it is almost incomprehensible to imagine how much so and what will happen next.

It would be hard to argue that Moore's law will continue indefinitely into the future. Nothing doubles forever, but for at least the next number of doubles, research and roadmaps on existing silicon technology indicate that the rate will continue. With theoretical limits on how many transistors could be placed on silicon chips, it wouldn't be a bad assumption to envision Moore's law or something like it actually slowing over time before accelerating again to a new technology. Nature often resembles a sigmoid function curve when stretched out over a longer time horizon. S curves resemble an S shape where growth is first quite slow, then exponential, and then it slows before reaching another step change, which creates the new S of exponential rate before slowing again. You could imagine a letter S stacked upon itself. Even as Moore's law invariably slows, newer technology like quantum computing, alternative materials to silicon, or any number of other technologies currently being researched could easily allow that rate of compute power to exponentially accelerate again. The slower growth between cycles will accelerate as well, and even though it will not technically be Moore's law, it will act similar.

Sigmoid Function Curve of Technology

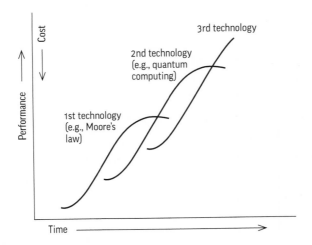

Even without continued exponential growth driven by Moore's law, we have already entered an accelerated cycle of learning and improvement, one that builds on the previous waves of innovation. Computing today has already connected much of the world and, as a result, made communication seamless. And much of the data and knowledge we are building on has been digitized. With fast, continuous communication, digitized data can be accessed at little or no cost. And unlike analogue information—from oral traditions to photocopies—digitized data does not lose fidelity as it is reproduced or moved. Once digitized, stored and backed up to the cloud, and subsequently backed up across data centres, information is there forever.

All of that digitization is also creating some impressive data capture, much more than we are even aware of, and the data collection from connected computers, people, cameras, and sensors has only just started. Connecting those devices to learn from data is arguably a far easier job than that of building the original network. The rate of growth in today's deep learning in artificial intelligence is largely driven by data collection and large data sets. In fact, every platform company today is really a data company with AI at its core. Other data, too, is moving out of its previous silos, giving rise to an intelligence that can be combined with other data sets to learn at a rate far faster than humans.

Much of the technology that exists today was only science fiction a couple of decades ago. I remember my first computer and Internet connection with a dial-up modem: the screeching sound of a land line and modem trying to connect, followed by a painfully slow experience loading each page of content. Today's fourth-generation wireless is, on average, 100 times as fast as my dial-up modem. But that speed, too, will soon feel as slow as my old modem. Fifth-generation networks (5G), starting to roll out in 2019, promise a twenty times increase in speed to what we have today.[22]

Today, through a simple cellphone and set of interfaces, many people have more power at their fingertips than leaders of countries had only thirty years ago. Technology has changed our lives so much that we take it for granted—we get frustrated when our wifi won't transfer in two seconds what would have taken twenty minutes in the year 2000. I still remember travelling through Southeast Asia and India in my youth and not being able to speak to my parents by phone for weeks at a time. Today, a technology development company I cofounded in India does daily Zoom video stand-ups with other teams from all over the world. Information that would have taken a skilled researcher with special access hours, days, or weeks to find in the 1990s can now be Googled in seconds. In a new city, instead of driving to a gas station to buy a map, and then trying to find the right route on the map, we can easily navigate using Waze or any number of other apps that give us directions visually and by voice in addition to time delays, red light cameras, and other important information. All of this comes free with a cellphone connection.

Remember that the underpinnings of the technology revolution are continuing to double. There are developments on the horizon that will make what we have now look primitive. And many of these technologies are not independent. They feed back to each other, which in turn drives more acceleration. For example, the same data captured through visualization in self-driving cars, drones, or robots provides more data to the network to learn faster. If it feels like it's hard keeping up with the rate of progress today, just wait for what's to come.

Technological advances have been hugely beneficial, enhancing our ability to live our lives better. As we are seeing, though, most of our jobs today come from the same inefficiencies and waste that technology replaces over the longer term.

And all of it is undermining the very basis of our economies: growth and inflation.

Let's take a deeper look at three technologies that should be entering the mainstream in the not-too-distant future. You are likely very aware of these technologies, but because adoption is still quite early, beyond the hype, their impact on society so far has been limited.

Self-driving cars

We have come a long way since the first DARPA Grand Challenge launched in 2004 to spur development of the first fully autonomous ground vehicles. None of the entrants in that first contest even finished the race. Fifteen years later, the time is nearing when truly autonomous self-driving automobiles will start their march across industries.

The Society of Automobile Engineers (SAE) has developed a classification of six levels of autonomous driving:

Level 0—A human driver is needed to control everything. Braking, speed, steering, etc.

Level 1—Most systems are still controlled by the driver but specific ones like steering or speed could be handled automatically.

Level 2—The driver can disengage from both steering and acceleration/deceleration at the same time. The system uses information about the environment. The driver must always be ready to take control of the vehicle.

Level 3—The driver is still required to take control if alerted, but level 3 is the first level that drivers can shift safety-critical features to the vehicle in some traffic and environmental conditions. The attention required from the driver in previous levels is no longer required.

Level 4—This is the first level that is fully autonomous, meaning that a driver is not required at all. The caveat is that it does not cover all driving environments.

Level 5—This is full autonomy on all driving conditions, including extreme environments. No steering wheel is required.

As of early 2019, most cars on the road are still at level 1, with a few examples of cars (such as Tesla's) that have already reached level 2 autonomy. Tesla and Audi (with its A8) are likely soon to be the first companies to offer level 3 autonomy—where drivers can take their eyes off the road—on the general market. Waymo, the company owned by Alphabet and GM, leads the pack on level 4, having tested millions of miles of driving in California and Arizona. Instead of focusing their first efforts on the general market, they have instead focused on taxis. Rollout will start slow, but it will feed back on itself and expand quickly. With global research and development budgets accelerating in the field, level 4 autonomy should be widespread by 2025.

The current utilization rate of an automobile is estimated at 5 percent. This means that 95 percent of the time you own your car, it sits idle in a parking garage or driveway. The entire automotive sector currently produces and sells cars to support a market of individuals using them only 5 percent of the time. Access changes the requirement for ownership, so autonomous driving is likely to significantly increase the utilization rate of cars. Here's why: if I can have a car whenever I need it without requiring a driver, I am likely to either 1) decide not to buy a car because I have access to a car whenever needed or 2) if I do buy a car, allow it to be used by others to help me pay for the asset I own. With either choice, utilization rates on cars should move much higher. That means that current forecasts of continually increasing demand for automobiles are very wrong. Instead, automotive production, and the jobs with it, could fall by 50 percent or more as autonomous cars move into the mainstream. Automotive companies, instead of making money through the sale and service of vehicles, will need to adjust their models to remain viable. Most likely that adjustment will have them selling cars as a service option, similar to software-as-a-service models in technology delivery today.

Those aren't the only second- and third-order effects of self-driving cars. As much as riders have benefitted from great new services, it is difficult to see how the ride-sharing companies, such as Uber or Lyft are going to make money in the future. The same key consideration for how to decrease their costs and increase their profits by removing drivers (automation) is going to make them compete against automotive manufacturers reinventing their models to stay in business. A utilization rate increase means less demand for automobiles. When manufacturers can give a choice of 1) a rides-on-demand service for a monthly fee or 2) an ability, when I purchase, to make extra dollars on my car when I'm not using it by adding my vehicle back to the network, what advantage do Uber and Lyft provide?

This would turn car manufacturers into platform companies. A business like this will follow a very similar trajectory to other technology platform businesses, since the new model enjoys network effects. That race is important because density of the network (availability and choice of car types) will be the main consideration to rapid adoption. Like most technology platforms that give rise to network effects, more cars on the platform (in each region) will create more value for consumers, which make it highly likely that the industry consolidates to one major platform winner.

It will also change our cities. Parking in cities is designed for the 5 percent utilization rate, meaning that the amount of parking designed into cities is staggering. According to a 2015 report, 14 percent of land in Los Angeles County is committed to parking.[23] You need room for parking while your car is at home as well as at each area that you and your car travel to: school, work, shopping, and so on. All of those parking spaces are often unused but are still required for peak times when needed. When the utilization rate of cars increases from 5 percent, the amount of storage needed to park cars while not in use plummets, which frees up valuable land—which will affect land use and prices, which will affect density, which will feed back on car use...

When you remove humans, you also remove human error. Approximately 94 percent of automotive accidents are caused by human error. According to the National Safety Council, in the United States, "The estimated cost of motor-vehicle deaths, injuries, and property damage in 2017 was $413.8 billion. The costs include wage and productivity losses, medical expenses, administrative expenses, employer costs, and property damage."[24] As autonomous driving enters mainstream adoption, it will reduce this figure significantly. Already, automotive companies such as Waymo and Tesla promise to underwrite their own insurance—an obvious nod to their belief in the technology being superior to human drivers. Insurance companies themselves at some point fall victim to a trend that doesn't have the same risks.

While I've focused on the example of the automotive sector, this same technology used in automotive—visualization, mapping, avoidance of obstacles—is entering the market for business applications such as trucking and delivery services. A technology that reduces costs so significantly and produces better outcomes is again deflationary in nature and, because of market incentives, impossible to stop. For now, we have both the overhead of the existing legacy system in drivers (more than 3 percent of the United States workforce are drivers), manufacturing capacity to produce for the 5 percent utilization rate, insurance, and accidents, combined with all of the new investment in autonomous vehicles. That means that today's job numbers and growth rates of the economy are much higher than they will be in the future as the legacy system is transitioned to the new.

The deflationary forces of the transition have not even begun to be experienced. For example, self-driving cars today still require oversight from a human operator because of regulation requiring someone to sit in the seat and be paid even if never called upon. As the cars themselves do the jobs better than humans, the endgame is inevitable. We will not have both system costs. With the technology moving into the mainstream, the transition will happen and drive much waste and cost out of the system. This can be great for humanity. The problem is that waste and cost are today's jobs.

Virtual and augmented reality

Today we are glued to our phones as an interface to our technology world: according to Deloitte, in 2018 the average user checked their smartphone fifty-two times a day.[25] But we will soon be more absorbed in it. Virtual and augmented reality (mixed reality) will offer a different, more immersive connection with our technology, and it will change the way many things are done.

Take, for example, a startup in Vancouver called LlamaZOO, which is in a new category of data collection called spatial data that is at the intersection of digital twinning (an exact twin of the physical world that is digital), mixed reality, and business intelligence. By twinning the real world via satellite imagery, drones, and lidar, and adding global positioning, mapping, and other data streams, the company uses mixed reality to reduce the cost of planning and work in the physical world. It allows for remote analyzing of massive amounts of data without traversing faraway sites with people. The company already counts big names such as Teck Resources, Goldcorp, and Chevron as clients. In one case study, LlamaZOO saved more than $55 million annually for a large forest company by interactively surveying regions for individual trees' heights for harvesting and by analyzing the best design of roads to reduce impact. Those savings come directly from inefficiencies in travel, surveying, and mistakes caused by not seeing the integrated information. And all of those savings are measured in jobs today.

For those who have experienced the leading edge of this technology, it feels like something that is hard to "unsee." By that, I mean that it is difficult to explain how quickly you forget about the headset you are wearing and completely experience a different world, one that feels very real. Having personally spent time in Redmond at the Microsoft HoloLens lab, and walking around on a virtual Mars that won NASA's software of the year award, I can tell you that travelling to Mars via virtual reality is an experience that is hard to put into words. The software allows collaboration and interaction through virtual avatars.

I was sitting about ten feet away at the Code Conference in 2016 when Elon Musk famously discussed the probability of us all living in a simulation. He explained his thesis, which was first introduced by Nick Bostrom, philosopher and author of the book *Superintelligence*, by using virtual reality/augmented reality as an example. He went on to argue that fidelity in virtual reality is already nearing fidelity of the real world (it feels real) and continuing to advance at a remarkable pace. If it feels real (or almost real) today and is progressing quickly, the chances are quite high that as the technology gets better and we use it more, the lines blur between reality and virtual reality, and we get confused about which reality we are in. Musk went on to ask what the chances are that this is the first time we have created this technology, making the case that if it were not the first time, we would not know it because we were part of a simulation. He then went on to conclude that he thought that "there is a billion to one chance that we are living in base reality."

Whatever reality we're living in, we're developing a very realistic next level of virtual reality. At what point does virtual or mixed reality become so good that it dramatically changes how we live our lives? For example, is it that difficult to imagine a world where people spend more of their time in mixed reality and less time travelling? Many other industries have been toppled as the digital experience and convenience becomes better than the analogue version. We don't believe it can happen because our minds project the present reality to the future, dismissing the present technology as inconsequential. But when we can genuinely feel the rush of skiing the Alps in the morning and the quiet of a beach cabana in Fiji in the afternoon with interactions like we were really there, would we still endure the hassle of waiting in lines at airports, travel, and lost baggage to experience it for real? And why should we expect the travel industry to act differently than other industries in transition to digital?

Why does that matter? According to the World Travel and Tourism Council, in 2018, travel contributed $8.8 trillion and 319 million jobs to the global economy. Entire local economies have become reliant on tourist dollars. What will they do if travelling slows?

Additive manufacturing and 3D printing

To the general population, the promise of anything we want printed right before our eyes vanished with the first wave of 3D printers that only printed crude versions of knickknacks. That image, of a printer slowly layering plastic into a rudimentary product, has been etched into our minds because the reality was so far away from the promise. Many of us, me included, dismissed a world where anything could be printed in our living rooms as a faraway dream, and the hype cycle of additive manufacturing ended.

But it was really only starting. The relentless march of technology innovation continued, and today the state of additive manufacturing is vastly different. Now commercially viable for a wide range of applications, the industry is moving fast, having surpassed $7.3 billion in 2017, according to Wohlers Associates.[26] Although not yet seen by the public commercially, it is just starting to reach a tipping point. I visited Carbon's additive manufacturing facility in California recently and was blown away. It was surreal to see the new Adidas shoe, the Yeezy, being printed—manufactured—out of liquid. I have visited hundreds of manufacturers around the world, and this manufacturing facility looked like none I had ever seen.

And in addition to speeds of printing that are improving exponentially, the list of materials that can be used in additive manufacturing grows by leaps and bounds every year. From metal to glass to food to cells to new nano-materials, the things that can already be produced is only limited by our imagination. What started in fast prototyping of designs has already moved into and replaced some traditional manufacturing for high cost/low volume parts; it can increase the quality and performance of designs while costing less. The aerospace, automotive, and medical industries, because of their performance needs, have all been early adopters. Additive manufacturing is now used to make lighter, more efficient engines, turbines, and other parts.

With continued technological acceleration, we can expect improvements on what is currently possible plus steep price declines resulting in industry-wide adoption. At some point along that curve, most—if not all—manufacturing will be disrupted. With digital files of your favourite products and dramatically lower costs, printing an object in the future should be as easy and cost effective as printing a document today. Network effects and a significant advantage to buyers in the form of cost savings, quality, and convenience will mean that what will start slow will accelerate quickly. Just like getting all the information on Google for free, a day will come where almost anything you could want is available to be printed on demand.

Most of the cost of the products we buy today is in the production, finance, storage, and transportation as goods are produced en masse and shipped around the world. In a world where it becomes much more economical to print locally, the entire infrastructure that exists to support movement and storage of goods will no longer be needed. That entire structure will collapse. Along with that collapse go all of the jobs that supported it.

And when it comes to trade wars and tariffs, how do governments collect a tax on a digital image that could be uploaded from anywhere and printed perfectly anywhere else?

These are not isolated pockets of disruption anymore. Not just one industry or market but all of them—together—at the same time, because the backbone that our future is built upon is technology. And that's not all. So far, we have looked only at the technologies through a narrow lens. The next three chapters look in depth at solar power and artificial intelligence, two horizontal technologies that will truly change everything about how we live. Their adoption will in some way or another power almost everything else—giving us the continuing doubling of technology progress and, as a natural derivative of it, a doubling of the deflation rate in prices falling and jobs disappearing.

All of these wonderful technologies make many things easier and cheaper. They increase efficiency and decrease costs, which means they are deflationary. They also remove the need for people to do many things—in other words, they get rid of jobs. If there is no net job creation globally (more global jobs created than destroyed), the inflationary system that we have relied on for commerce throughout history cannot continue.

The coming sonic boom

By any measure, the only thing driving economic growth is easy credit and debt. If the only way to keep growing is through the addition of more and more debt that cannot be repaid, can we honestly say that we have an economic system that still works? It turns out that technology isn't the only thing that is exponential. The only way to keep our economies growing and combat the effect of that exponential technology under the existing system is to allow debt to rise exponentially as well.

The effects of deflation from technology cannot be outrun by piling on ever more debt in a hopeless effort to keep economies thriving and drive more jobs. In an ironic twist, this forces our societies to compete for a limited amount of high-paying jobs to stay on the hamster wheel of rising prices. At the same time, technology companies act quickly to implement more technology that removes jobs quicker, since they cannot compete with platforms otherwise. Unless global jobs and our economies expand at a rate that exceeds debt creation (which even at backwards-looking rates of progress seems impossible), the age of inflation is already over. We just don't know it yet.

It took $185 trillion of debt to produce about $46 trillion of GDP growth over the last twenty years. The growth rate would likely have been negative without all of that stimulus. How much so is impossible to tell. Asset prices would be far lower as well. (For all the Keynesians reading this, please refrain from jumping to any conclusion yet.) So what comes next?

The majority of the deflation is still in front of us—driven by technology advancing at an exponential rate. If we are doubling our rate of progress on technology every eighteen months or so, and that technology is deflationary, then it is also logical to expect if it "only" took $185 trillion of debt over the last twenty years to fight the deflation and drive growth, then it might take that number again, but this time over the next thirty-six or so months. And eighteen months after that, a further $370 trillion.

Remember, the world of 2018 has approximately $250 trillion in debt to run an $80 trillion world economy. That debt in itself is a massive drag on future growth because of interest payments on it. What about when we add another $555 trillion? With the incredible amount of debt today, slowing growth or asset price deflation would create a brutally negative feedback cycle where things unwind very quickly. Quite plausibly, to keep driving growth against an exponentially increasing technology deflation, global debt could become a number so high that the only way out is to hit the reset button. The truth is we have probably already passed that point at which a complete reset is required. Our technology boom will cause another kind of boom.

At approximately 1,239 kilometres per hour, the speed of a jet surpasses the speed of sound, and because the sound waves can't push in front of it any longer, it punches through the sound barrier, causing a loud boom—and changing the rules. After that, from the ground the plane appears to outrun its sound. The metaphor of a sonic boom is akin to what we will see at some point with debt creation when the rules will change instantly. But for now, the pain of an asset unwind and negative feedback cycle means that governments will try to stop it by all means necessary. With many countries still today in negative interest rate territory, where money deposited in the banks is guaranteed to lose money, and governments realizing that another crisis is just around the corner, ever more creative solutions are being seriously explored.

In an August 2018 working paper titled "Monetary Policy with Negative Interest Rates" by the International Monetary Fund, the authors discuss how central banks can design and operate a system where interest rates could be far more negative than they are today. As interest rates drop too far below zero, it makes sense for deposit holders to move their money out of banks and into cash, resulting in a limit to how low central banks can reduce interest rates, as people and businesses will hoard cash. The proposed solution sees a mechanism where negative exchange rates are applied to both electronic money in reserves as well as cash—so cash would be taxed at the same negative interest rate.[27] We can deduce the following couple of points insofar as there is serious discussion on how to manipulate currencies even further: 1) drastic below-zero interest rates will be needed, and 2) we have seriously lost the plot!

We should therefore expect more easing, and more chaos from it, as the can is kicked down the road once again. Again, as Nassim Nicholas Taleb points out in his book *Antifragile*, "Systematically preventing forest fires from taking place 'to be safe' makes the big one much worse." The second-order effects in the form of rising nationalism and political instability are also likely to become much worse.

It is important to understand that all of that debt did have a very positive effect on our economies, jobs, and lives. As we talked about in chapter 1 on how the economy works, when asset prices rise, people feel richer and spend more, which in turn creates more jobs because their spending drives the economy. Growth would not have been nearly the same without it and, therefore, many of the benefits to society would not have accumulated as quickly without it. The number of people in the world living in extreme poverty—earning under $1.90 per day—has fallen significantly, from more than 50 percent of the world fifty years ago to under 10 percent of the world's population today.[28] Long-term trends in life expectancy, infant mortality, and a host of other measures are also positive.

Easy credit resulted in a significant rise in prices across asset classes—home prices, oil prices, stock prices, to name a few—creating real wealth for the holders of assets and spurring even more growth, with countless jobs being added to growth sectors of the economy that have been aided by easy credit and low rates. Venture capital and technology companies themselves have benefitted greatly from this cheap source of capital in raising giant venture rounds, meaning that some of the technology progress and feedback loops themselves were quite likely accelerated beyond what would have otherwise been possible.

But that boom has now led to another boom, a phase shift where all the rules change.

The simple power of technology is that it allows for abundance without the same amount of jobs or income ... if we let it. It is a fact that we better get used to if we want that same abundance in our lives.

5

THE FUTURE
OF ENERGY

W
HAT IF YOU could buy a permanent source of electricity for your house for $2 million? What if the price dropped from $2 million to under $100? And you only have to pay that once and, forever after, all your electricity would be free—like the air you breathe?

At what point along that price-versus-value curve would your consumption of energy change? That choice will drive the future of energy and it has the potential to change our lives in a very positive way. But it, too, is deflationary and will drastically change our economies.

There is no life on Earth without energy. Every living plant or creature on Earth consumes energy for its survival. We use it for making products, for transportation, for heating, cooling, and lighting, and for growing, processing, and storing food. It is often the most important input cost in production and distribution, and therefore, its use has a huge impact on the competitiveness and growth of our economies. Energy costs often determine economic viability. As a result, energy is naturally a very large part of our economies, coming in at about 9 percent of GDP globally.[29]

At 9 percent of GDP, it makes up a lot of jobs around the world. In the US alone, 3.6 million direct jobs are in the traditional energy industries, including production, transmission, and storage, with another approximately two million jobs in energy efficiency.[30] But the role of energy in our economies is much higher than that. We still need to factor in how much of the world's military complex is built mainly to ensure continual access to energy at reasonable prices. Low-price, abundant energy is a critical component of any nation's competitiveness, since it is used in every industry. Beyond that, we must factor in the damage cost of extreme weather events and flooding due to climate change, which is, at its root, caused by the way we extract and use energy today. And those costs—from insurance increases to clean-up and rebuilding—also contribute to our economies.

Not surprisingly, much research has claimed a direct linkage with energy consumption and economic growth, with more advanced societies using more energy per capita.[31] This makes intuitive sense: if energy is central to economic activity, we can expect energy use to go up along with economic activity. And it has. Since 1900, energy use has skyrocketed. Worldwide energy use has gone up almost thirteen times, from

12,100 terawatt hours per year in 1900 to 153,596 terawatt hours in 2017. The biggest drivers were cheap and abundant sources of energy: coal, crude oil, and natural gas. From 1900 to 2017, coal as a primary source of energy grew from 5,728 to 43,397 terawatt hours, crude oil grew from 181 to 53,752 petawatt hours (a petawatt hour is 1,000 terawatt hours), and natural gas grew from 64 to 36,704 terawatt hours.[32]

The laws of energy

Before we talk about where we are going with respect to energy, let's look at how we got to where we are. To do that, we need to explore two fundamental facts: the first and second laws of thermodynamics.

The first law of thermodynamics states that energy cannot be created or destroyed and that the total amount of energy in the universe must remain the same. It can be changed, stored, or moved, but it can't be created or destroyed. James Prescott Joule (1818–1899) discovered that the transformation of mechanical work (energy) to heat happens in fixed proportions. In his famous experiment, he let a weight of 890 pounds fall one foot on a pulley turning a paddlewheel in water, and he found that the water increased in temperature by one degree. This gave rise to the first mechanical measure of heat, which was energy being transferred but not created or destroyed.

The second law of thermodynamics states that energy always moves from higher to lower concentrations. In other words, heat dissipates. The energy of the sun moves to space. The energy from a boiling pot converts to steam and then into cooler air. Furthermore, all transfer of energy in a *closed* system creates a more and more disordered state—more entropy. Because each time energy is transformed, some or all of it is wasted as it disperses from higher concentrations to lower ones.

You can see the effect of this in our planet today. Most of our energy sources are fossil fuels, which are taken from a closed system (our planet), which according to the second law of thermodynamics must create more entropy or disorder as we use them. Take a typical car as an example. Consider the journey of getting gasoline to your tank so your engine has fuel to move you. First, an exploration company needs to dig for and find oil, using energy to do so. Remember, that oil as an "energy source" has only been stored. The energy in oil initially came through plants that absorbed their own energy from the sun through photosynthesis, and through animals that absorbed their energy by feeding on the plants. All of that energy originally came from the sun. That oil needs to be pumped from the ground (requiring energy) and transported (requiring energy) to an oil refinery, where it undergoes a conversion (requiring energy) to gasoline. That gasoline then needs to be transported (requiring energy) to a regional gas station where you fill your car. Even the most efficient internal combustion engines only convert between 25 and 50 percent of the energy in gasoline into moving the car; up to 75 percent of the energy is emitted as heat and carbon dioxide and released into the atmosphere.

Through this example, you can see a fuller cost of the energy to move your car. It includes a staggering amount of inefficiency... and drives countless jobs. As the second law of thermodynamics tells us, each time energy is converted, more and more of it is wasted—dissipated (not destroyed). And in our case, it is converted—and moved—often. Much of our economy is driven by that exploration, extraction, conversion, and movement—either directly or indirectly.

How we got here is completely understandable. Throughout human history, the process of energy extraction and use from digging up the energy that had been stored in plants and animals and then converting that energy for our use caused damage to our environment, but the size of our populations and subsequent energy use meant we couldn't see the damage to the environment as easily as we can today. As well, partly because we couldn't see the damage caused, it made economic sense. Even if producing much of the that energy was inefficient and wasteful, the energy sources—wood, coal, oil, and natural gas—were abundant and inexpensive.

But our energy needs today are much greater than they were in years past, and the cumulative damage from the use of inefficient energy is likewise greater. We stay on a wheel of inefficiency where our economies are addicted to the jobs and profits derived from exploiting energy—ignoring the fully loaded cost of fossil fuels when we include its by-product, global warming. As well, we fail to predict how different things will be as energy costs drop to a point where that entire existing energy infrastructure becomes irrelevant because of market pricing. We stay in a feedback loop not unlike our debt spiral: we do not see the true cost to our societies because we want to keep the party going, and we can't imagine an alternative to the way we have built our economies.

Let the sun shine in

By getting our energy directly from the sun instead of a circuitous route of digging things up that originally got their energy from the sun and transforming and re-transforming them, we remove an entire supply chain of inefficiency and cost. By converting energy from the sun directly, we can get an almost-free lunch... without the corresponding damage to our ecosystem. In less than two hours, more energy from the sun hits the Earth than the yearly worldwide consumption of energy.[33] It's just a question of putting it to use.

The photovoltaic effect (light being absorbed by a material and creating an electric current) was first discovered in 1839 by French scientist Edmond Becquerel (1820–1891). It took over forty years before Charles Fritts (1850–1903), an American inventor, created the world's first rooftop solar array. Another sixty years passed before Bell Labs invented the modern solar cell in 1954. Made from silicon, this breakthrough cell had 6 percent efficiency in converting sunlight to energy, which was a huge improvement from previous technologies. It allowed solar to be used for about $256 per watt. Even with that huge leap forward, $256 per watt was far more expensive than other sources of energy at the time, so it is easy to see why a transition from lower-cost sources of energy to solar power didn't take place.

As technology has improved, though, that rate has dropped precipitously, from $256 per watt in 1954 to 82 cents today. (When we adjust for inflation—convert 1954 dollars to today's dollars—the drop is equivalent to solar dropping from $2,108.00 to $0.82 per watt.) Many have compared the advance we're seeing in solar energy to Moore's law. While different than Moore's law because it relates to manufacturing scale, Swanson's law (named after Richard Swanson, founder of SunPower) states that the price of solar tends to drop 20 percent for every doubling of shipped volume. At present trends of shipped volume, it suggests that costs will fall by 75 percent every ten years.

And the cost of solar panels per watt allows output of energy indefinitely—until the failure of the device. Unlike many other forms of energy that require extensive operating and maintenance costs, the cost to maintain solar is low. A typical coal-fired power plant has a large capital cost and a life of about forty years. Solar installations should extend well beyond forty years, and they are far less expensive to operate— you don't have to dig up and ship sunlight to them, for one thing. According to a research report by financial think tank Carbon Tracker in November 2018, 42 percent of the world's coal plants are already running at a loss, and it costs 35 percent more to keep existing coal plants running than to build new renewable energy generators.[34] If these numbers are true, due to economic realities and competition, the days of coal as a source of energy are numbered.

When comparing energy costs between sources, the most common measure is the levelized cost of energy (LCOE), which allows firms to understand the total cost of energy, including building and maintenance costs divided by the lifetime of power production. According to Wall Street investment bank Lazard, which runs yearly research on the energy sector, the levelized cost of utility-grade solar dropped 88 percent in the last ten years.[35] Last year alone, prices fell by another 13 percent, bringing LCOE in solar to among the lowest of all energy sources. Will pricing continue to fall at that rate? It's impossible to say for certain, but I'll bet that Swanson's law will keep holding true—we will continue to see the rate of improvement that we have been seeing over the last forty years. Why? Simply because of economics. Because energy is an input cost to almost everything, cheaper sources of energy give significant advantages to both companies and economies. As the economic advantage shifts to solar, a gold rush of innovation and capacity building shifts with it, as an entire industry looks to win a new strategic market. And markets that seemingly don't change at all will change very quickly. As Mark Lewis of BNP Paribas Asset Management wrote, "We conclude that the economics of oil for gasoline and diesel vehicles versus wind- and solar-powered EVs are now in relentless and irreversible decline, with far-reaching implications for both policymakers and the oil majors."[36]

I should say that there are other very good clean energy sources, but solar is the one that has the potential to exceed (by a large margin) the amount of energy needed for our world. As Jeff Tsao of the US Department of Energy and his colleagues Nate Lewis and George Crabtree explained, "Though wind has significant extractable potential, its technical potential is much less, in large part because much of its power resides geographically over the relatively inaccessible deep oceans. The same is true for solar, but because its extractable potential is so huge, its land-based technical potential remains large."[37]

How much area would be required to build solar farms to generate all of our needed energy? Without taking into consideration any improvement in technology, according to the renewable energy advocacy group Land Art Generator, the surface area required is 496,805 square kilometres.[38] That may sound like a lot of land, but the land leased to the oil and gas industry in the United States alone covers 104,177 square kilometres.[39] If you used that land for solar power, you could provide more than one-fifth of the world's entire energy needs.

The days of abundant, almost-free solar power are coming. Prices of solar are already lower than almost all other forms of energy, and prices will continue to fall much further with technology advancements and as solar reaches mass adoption. While other sources of energy are still needed because solar contribution is small in totality, from here it is only a matter of transition time. In 2000, solar only accounted for 1.15 terawatt hours of electricity; by 2017, that had grown to 443 terawatt hours. Solar is still a very long way away from producing 100 percent of the 153,596 terawatt hours energy needed today, but with lower price on its side, and even lower pricing on the horizon, that gap will close quickly.

One of the greatest criticisms of solar and other renewables is that they are intermittent. The sun doesn't shine at night, and it can cloud over, meaning that there is too much power at certain times and not enough at others. Combine this with peak load requirements of populations—more energy is required at certain times of the day than others—and storage of that energy becomes an important issue. But along with ongoing innovations in battery technology to reduce this burden, there are other solutions making their way onto the market. One such solution—a flywheel—converts electricity to kinetic energy for storage and then converts kinetic energy back to electricity when needed. There's a new race to control key pieces of technology to enable a shift to abundant renewable power. For example, Temporal Power of Mississauga, Ontario, Canada, a leading innovator in the space, was recently acquired by the Chinese flywheel technology company BC New Energy.

The market opportunity in front of solar is staggering. And as investment rushes into it, in turn driving more innovation efficiency and further reduction in pricing and storage, the same cycle of creative destruction will drive investment out of coal, oil, and natural gas. In the short term, economies will have the benefit of both the solar infrastructure buildout as well as the other energy sources that are transitioning. But market forces will ensure that the far less expensive energy infrastructure will win—and with that win, the existing infrastructure of inefficiency and jobs will disappear.

Some developing countries may actually be at an advantage with respect to energy. Developing countries could avoid an entire infrastructure buildout to support energy, similarly to how millions of miles of telephone poles were not needed in Africa or Asia because of cellular technology, or how much faster China's ecommerce adoption grew than the United States' because they didn't have the existing infrastructure of retail stores to slow it down.

But as energy is a major input to almost everything, how could less expensive energy not be deflationary in nature? It will be massively so. If governments and central banks think they can outrun deflation today, when we are only starting to feel the effects of numerous technologies driven by Moore's law, what happens when we add to those numerous technologies the deflationary effects that abundant solar energy will bring? If the only way to stop deflation today is by turning on the money printing press, what will tomorrow look like?

Changing the price of tomorrow

What else changes because of energy prices that keep falling? Let's look at a couple of examples of things that might become completely different. Remember, energy price is often what determines economic viability, and as a result we likely discount the other things that are possible as energy is reduced in price.

An underlying reason for refugee crises and pressure on immigration in developed countries around the world is the scarcity of basic resources like food and water. With lower-cost or free energy, why couldn't there be there be an abundance of clean water? It's not that technology doesn't exist to convert salt water to fresh water. It has been around for decades; it just comes down to cost. The paradox of many coastal communities around the developing world is that even though they are surrounded by water, it is not usable for drinking or irrigation because of its salt content. Desalination—the removal of salt from sea water—is much more efficient today through the large-scale use of reverse osmosis, a process whereby salt water is pumped through a water-permeable membrane. But though readily available, it's not widely commercially viable because it takes a lot of energy: the operating pressures required are between 800 and 1,000 psi.[40] Lower-cost energy completely upends that dynamic, bringing with it clean water and all the other accompanying benefits for society— including helping to prevent the environmental conditions that can lead to wars and refugee crises.

Clean energy will stop adding more carbon dioxide to our environment, of course. Carbon dioxide emissions from the burning of fossil fuels have taken levels of greenhouse gases in our atmosphere to levels never before seen in human history: 415 parts per million. Ice core samples confirm it is a concentration not seen for more than 800,000 years. Carbon dioxide is one of the ways our planet stays warm: like bricks capturing heat from a warm summer's day and releasing it slowly, carbon dioxide in our environment does the same. At never-before-seen concentrations that are continuing to rise quickly, it is bound to get very warm. But what if abundant clean energy not only stops adding to that but helps to reverse it? Could the benefit of extraordinarily cheap power allow us to remove carbon dioxide from our environment efficiently?

Like desalinization except for in the air, carbon capture is already possible. In some large-scale coal energy plants, it is already a mandated requirement to reduce the amount of carbon dioxide that is released into the environment. But the process requires a huge amount of energy—increasing the amount of energy used by up to 40 percent—and that's at the tops of smoke stacks, where the carbon dioxide is most concentrated. But if renewable energy costs fall far enough, along with no longer needing the smoke stacks, could we not extend carbon capture into our everyday environment, where the concentration of carbon dioxide is lower?

The solutions so far also imagine a future where there is centralized power: vast solar installations with distribution from power companies similar to how such companies operate today. But one thing that we have already learned from technology advances in other areas is that it often changes where value is derived, making it so an existing monopoly cannot compete. Retail stores, for example, had monopoly power only until the Internet allowed far more choice than a physical store could hold. With power, too, we may see major disruption, and that disruption could come from anywhere.

Central utilities or power companies are essentially distribution companies, all about supply and demand, buying energy "supply" for one price and marking it up when selling and distributing it to cover the costs and profit. As solar advances, and price further declines, more consumers will choose to break from the grid in the same way those consumers are "cord cutting" from former cable television monopolies. They can turn to their own solar installations with their own backup storage. If they own electric cars, those batteries can contribute to their homes in peak times, and then the same solar power generation on the roof will refill that battery during the day if the sun is out and the car is not in use.

It is also quite possible that vast central energy planning grids may give way to generation that is local and interconnected broadly, in the same way that the Internet is a distributed technology with connected nodes, and this interconnection makes the Internet more reliable and secure. In this case, my home and other homes in my region could be a backup for when others or other regions are using energy, and vice versa.

The timing may still be uncertain, but the trend towards abundant renewable energy is not. That trend will bring with it a complete disruption to our existing energy infrastructure—and every one of the jobs that goes with that inefficiency. That can be a great thing for all of humanity… if we let the natural course of deflation take hold. For if we allow that to happen—instead of holding onto an inefficient system in order to pay higher prices for energy and keep now-irrelevant jobs—we will not need the jobs because we can get all the energy required for nearly free. We might be able to adjust to earning less money if everything we need costs less.

That's an important *if*.

6

THE FUTURE
OF INTELLIGENCE

"In from three to eight years, we will have a machine with
the general intelligence of an average human being."

MARVIN MINSKY in *LIFE* (1970)

LIKE MOST PREDICTIONS of technology, Minsky's proved to
be early. The doubling-up examples from chapter 4
show why: it is as easy to overestimate the impact of
exponential growth in the early doubles, as it is to
underestimate it in the later ones. Until relatively recently,
the promise of artificial intelligence far outpaced actual breakthroughs. But while he had the timing wrong, Minsky had
the right idea. Today artificial intelligence is already shaping
our future and it is about to move into many more domains.

But maybe not in ways even some of the top thought leaders see it.

The impact of artificial intelligence

In late 2018, I was invited to the Creative Destruction Lab/ University of Toronto's Rotman School of Management conference on machine learning and the market for intelligence. The conference is one of the top in the world on the state of machine intelligence/AI and is attended by some of the foremost thought leaders. In fact, many of the breakthroughs in artificial intelligence were created by Canadian researchers who continued working in the space through AI's dark winter of the '80s and '90s.

One of the speakers at the conference was Mark Carney, governor of the Bank of England. Carney explained that artificial intelligence is an example of a general purpose technology— by which he meant a technology that can affect an entire economy and drastically alter society. He compared it to electrification of the world in the early twentieth century. He explained how economies went through dramatic changes because many jobs were eliminated by electricity, and workers needed to be retrained for new jobs that hadn't existed before. He showed how, as electrification intensified, economies at first suffered and lost jobs, but then increasingly flourished as the new technology created new industries and countless new jobs for the transitioned workers.

While sitting in the audience, I couldn't help thinking that, while Carney was right about electricity being a general purpose technology, the analogous optimistic outlook for AI sounded like something that he wanted to be true, rather than something that had a high probability of actually coming true. Equating artificial intelligence to electricity was a bad comparison for a number of important reasons.

Firstly, electricity wasn't an exponential technology. It was an important breakthrough for humanity, but it did not double its effectiveness every eighteen months or so. More importantly, nobody ever thought electricity was going to be intelligent. Electricity was an incredible invention that enabled many other things to advance, but it was never on a path to being smarter than human beings. Artificial intelligence is nothing like electricity. If electricity was a match, artificial intelligence is the sun.

That difference brings a major risk in how we plan. If AI will create far more jobs in the future than are destroyed in the present, then there will need to be vast retraining of the population into new jobs. We can also expect social upheaval similar to what happened as electricity transitioned economies. It will be a tough time, but after that, jobs will reappear, and economies will flourish again. Many of the policy tools that worked in the past are likely to work again. But what if AI *doesn't* create more jobs in the future? What if it doesn't just take the ones in the near term but starts to take more and more jobs? The solutions we're putting in place today expecting a coming job boom could create a more dangerous world.

The boom could be like a sonic boom—with the jobs, like the sound waves, never catching up.

The timeline is important. Maybe general purpose artificial intelligence (where machines are smarter than us at everything) is still decades or more away, but it is not *if* but *when* it arrives. Artificial intelligence is only the natural next stage in a long trend of growth in information and knowledge, a growth that is doubling with the proliferation of technology. It will have a profound impact—far more profound than anything we have seen before.

Artificial intelligence is often conflated with superintelligence. But today, most of the success in AI is really machine learning or "narrow" artificial intelligence, not general purpose AI. The same AI that beats humans at chess cannot generalize and play *Jeopardy!* instead. But while it is easy to dismiss narrow AI and believe in our own superiority, artificial intelligence that can beat humans at different domains has enormous implications. We have only started to see its effects, and it will get better quickly and accelerate across industries—to the point where instead of training it, we are not needed.

Beyond this, though, researchers and businesses continue to work on artificial general intelligence (AGI): intelligence that can generalize and take knowledge from one domain to another. How far out is artificial general intelligence, where AI might be smarter than a human at all things? I asked Ben Goertzel, one of the preeminent researchers in AGI. Ben has spent much of his life thinking about AGI and working to create it. And in his estimation, we will have it within five to thirty years depending on how efforts are directed.

It's almost incomprehensible that in our own lifetimes, maybe even quite soon, our long-term reign at the top of the intelligence ladder will fall to machines. Until recently, that outcome seemed like science fiction. But the explosion in knowledge and the positive feedback loop from learning is accelerating to the point that we are finding it hard to keep up with the changes.

To see how computers could eventually outsmart humans, it is worth examining our own "intelligence" a little more deeply.

A brief history of intelligence

Our intelligence—our ability to master the world around us—is actually derived from other people: their thoughts, inventions, and science, which we have in turn continued to build upon. Without that information and knowledge, most of our limited time would go into providing basic human needs. Throughout our history, it is our collective growth of knowledge that is the real driver of what we deem "intelligence."

As we saw in chapter 3, our brains are imperfect storage devices. They do not remember events exactly as they happened. Instead of remembering only the facts, we remember events through our own biases, filters, and emotions. Our own minds are only capable of remembering what can be learned in a lifetime. Beyond that limit, we need external aids.

Imagine that you and a small group of others are exiled from the world to a remote island community where you can only pass on your knowledge through verbal communication.

Books and writing are unavailable. You have all your current knowledge but lack the tools of modern life. Phones, electricity, plumbing... all the conveniences you take for granted are gone. You have only what you know and a few basic necessities and are forced to recreate a civilization over time, generation by generation. On that imaginary island with no books, computers, or anything else, how many generations would it be until your descendants lost the vast amounts of information we take for granted to make our way in the world today and be, in that framework, considered "unintelligent"? Knowledge transmitted orally would lose fidelity over time, memories would fade, and things that were never mentioned would be forever forgotten. Your children would know a little less than you, and their children less than them, and so on. In a few short generations, life would be very different, as the inhabitants focused on basic survival needs and rituals designed to enable their most important stories to travel to the next generation.

There are real-life examples. The Sentinelese, of North Sentinel Island in the Indian Ocean, are one of the most isolated tribes in the world; they recently gained unwanted attention when they killed a missionary named John Allen Chau who came to their island. Although they have had contact with outsiders from time to time, in 1956, to protect their way of life, the government of India declared North Sentinel island a tribal reserve. Contact from the outside world is banned. As a small and isolated culture, cut off from the world, they have limited means to build up complex knowledge, and as a result, their way of life has been similar for generations.

There are more than 100 isolated tribes of the world today like the Sentinelese, mostly in densely forested areas in South America and Indonesia. The little information that we know about these tribes and their way of life looks very similar to what we know of prehistoric humans from hundreds of thousands of years ago. In fact, for approximately 300,000 years, our brains have remained largely unchanged.[41] These isolated and prehistoric people are as we could be—and vice versa.

What, then, changed to give us a staggering advance in this kind of "intelligence"?

We have had written language for millennia now, and it has enabled those who knew how to use it to increase their store of understanding. But a real phase shift started with Johannes Gutenberg's invention of movable type and the printing press in 1439. Gutenberg's press could be viewed as one of the most important inventions of humanity. Various forms of printing existed for hundreds of years beforehand, but they were slow, expensive, and as such only available to small parts of the population. The printing press led to the mass storage of information, effectively allowing the human brain to be extended to books where information could be recalled at will.

By 1500, there were already 20 million books printed, and over the next 100 years, there were estimated to be between 150 million and 200 million books in circulation.[42] This expansion of new ideas and an increasing literacy rate was the start of a revolution in ideas and knowledge. Besides allowing wide distribution, it also encouraged the criticism and debate of ideas. Religions of the world used the printing press to spread their beliefs, but it also set the stage for science-based reasoning. Authors could share their new ideas and have them tested and confirmed or refuted by others. The ability to do this, over time, developed into the scientific method. Although philosophers such as Aristotle (384–322 BCE) and Ibn al-Haytham (965–1040 CE) had used similar logic to describe the world around them, the process itself wasn't generally accepted as such until the late nineteenth century.

There is no one inventor of the scientific method. Like science itself, it continued to be refined thanks to the likes of Galileo, Bacon, Descartes, and Newton. The process involves 1) observation, including rigorous skepticism (to counter our cognitive biases); 2) formulating a hypothesis; 3) making a prediction that can be determined to be true or false; and 4) experiments and testing to determine the validity of the hypothesis. The process continually repeats, allowing better and better hypotheses to be tested and confirmed. Perhaps the most compelling thing about science and the scientific method is that it is almost never "good enough." It is designed to continually bring in more evidence to prove existing understanding wrong and to correct it further.

Error correction is the basis of all intelligence.

As Karl Popper (1902–1994), one of the great twentieth-century philosophers of science, said, "All of our knowledge grows only through the correcting of our mistakes."[43] Some of the biggest revolutions in science actually come from small refinements of existing theories. As Sir Isaac Newton said, "If I have seen further than other men, it is because I have stood on the shoulders of giants."[44] The biggest "giant" for Newton was Galileo: Newton's work that resulted in the three laws of motion was influenced by Galileo's work on forces.

The printing press recorded and stored information and, with it, delivered the ability to correct errors to a much wider audience. This gave rise to the Age of Enlightenment—also known as the Age of Reason. Starting in the late seventeenth century and extending through the eighteenth century, it was a time of transition, where philosophical and intellectual ideas—science and logic—started to undermine ideas of the Church, monarchy, and the reality of the times. French writer Voltaire observed that "it is dangerous to be right in matters where established men are wrong,"[45] but Voltaire and his peers persisted, and the newfound availability and durability of knowledge allowed new ways of being right to spread and prevail. Since those new ideas broke some of the foundations that established religion relied upon—like the Earth being at the centre of the universe—other long-held doctrines also came into question, further weakening the enormous power the Church had over everyday life and paving the way for more science-based reasoning and greater contribution from society, which propelled innovation at an even faster rate.

In a world that seems more divisive with each passing day, it is worth remembering that intellectual debate to find better answers is the goal of science and the very thing that has allowed great leaps forward for mankind. To quote Karl Popper again, "True ignorance is not the absence of knowledge, it's the refusal to acquire it."[46]

Because of the combined ability to both make a permanent record of our knowledge and have our ideas continually questioned and built upon, humanity's ability to understand our world has seemed to change overnight on the evolutionary scale. Remember, our brains have been almost the same for around 300,000 years, but we've had the printing press for just under 600 years.

Just like the exponential effect of pennies doubling or grains of rice on a chessboard, extending our brains to books and refining and extending ideas that came before us allowed our knowledge to increase exponentially. At first, it was seemingly slow and small, a metaphorical trickle of information. Now there is a flood of information and knowledge that is hard to comprehend and keep up with. Far more information is being created and shared every second than any one of us could learn and communicate in a lifetime. The more information there is, the more correction it needs—but the same exponential growth of technology that allows this explosion of information also allows exponentially improved error correction: a sonic boom of information and knowledge, with our computers getting further and further ahead of us.

The beginning of AI

Try to imagine yourself living in the early to mid-1800s: horse-drawn carriages, no telephones, before the electrification of cities. It is hard to even comprehend that the designs for a modern-day computer could be envisioned then, but Charles Babbage (1791–1871), a British polymath, did just that.

Babbage found errors while reviewing astronomical tables that were calculated by hand, and he realized that computational problems were dangerous to navigation. So, he devised a solution and created the first blueprint for a mechanical-based computation. In 1822, Babbage set out to create a "difference engine," which was strictly a calculator. Although the engine was never finished during Babbage's life, in 2002, the Science Museum in London completed two versions of Babbage's original designs of the difference engine, using Babbage's own designs and only parts available from the era. Each engine consists of 8,000 parts, weighs five tons, and measures eleven feet long by seven feet high.[47] Babbage later used the knowledge he gained while designing the difference engine to prototype his analytics engine. It was the first design of a general purpose computer, with many of the functions that our computers have, including separate storage and central processing, and areas for inputting and outputting data and instructions. He was a long way ahead of his time and, again, the prototypes were actually never completed during his lifetime due to funding constraints. (Plan28.org is an ongoing project to use his designs to build his analytics engine using only parts available from his time. That project is on track to finish by 2021.)

Advances in technology—including electricity—increased what was possible. Research into thinking machines grew from the 1930s to 1950s. An important trailblazer of the time was Alan Turing (1912-1954), an English mathematician. Turing is best known for breaking the German Enigma code in

World War II, which allowed the Allies to read encrypted messages crucial to their victory over Nazi Germany—a feat depicted in the movie *The Imitation Game*. But he was also an early believer that the human brain was in large part a digital computing machine, and therefore that computers could be made to have intelligence—to think. In 1950, he published a paper titled "Computing Machinery and Intelligence" where he proposed a test called the imitation game, now commonly referred to as the Turing test. In the test, a human evaluator would have a conversation with two others, one being a machine and one a human, and the test would be passed when the human evaluator could not distinguish between the human and machine—in short, when humans can't distinguish artificial from real intelligence.

Around the same time that Turing was publishing "Computing Machinery and Intelligence," another eminent thinker named Claude Shannon (1916–2001) was breaking barriers that enabled many of the advances in computers and artificial intelligence that we now take for granted. Shannon was an American mathematician and one of the main architects of the Information Age. Although not as well known, his breakthroughs rival Albert Einstein's in that he changed the way we think about information.

Shannon was interested in how to transmit information in its simplest form and realized that to do so, information must not be confused with meaning. We rarely hear information in exactly the same way the person sending us the information means it; instead, we attach our own emotion to the information and often change the message as a result. Our context is also an important factor: for example, the word "Amazon" might take on a completely different meaning for a hearer in Seattle, the location of the company Amazon's headquarters, than for one in in Brazil, where the Amazon River is the heart of a rainforest covering 70 percent of the country. For Shannon, "These semantic aspects of communication are irrelevant to the engineering problem. The significant aspect is that the actual message is one *selected from a set* of possible messages."[48] He went on to describe how information could be sent using partial messages that give clues to the original message. For example, if a message tells you a number is between 1 and 100, and then the next message tells you the number is odd, you can cut the possibilities in half.

Shannon was also the first to ascribe entropy to communication, and the information in each of these partial messages became a measure for how much uncertainty it resolved for the receiver. By doing so, he invented a unit of measure for information, the bit. In partial messages, one bit of information cuts the number of possibilities in half for the receiver. A message that doesn't reduce the possibilities for the receiver transmits zero bits of information. Because of Shannon's information theory, for the first time, information became quantifiable. Measuring information and its growth became as easy as measuring anything else, and information processing, storage, and retrieval were born.

As computers and storage of information made it possible to analyze more information, artificial intelligence research was born at a workshop at Dartmouth College in 1956. Allen Newell, Herbert Simon, John McCarthy, Marvin Minsky, and Arthur Samuel were the first participants and became the founding leaders of AI research. Their original research proposal reads as follows: "The study is to proceed on the basis of the conjecture that every aspect of learning or any other feature of intelligence can in principle be so precisely described that a machine can be made to simulate it. An attempt will be made to find how to make machines use language, form abstractions and concepts, solve kinds of problems now reserved for humans, and improve themselves. We think that a significant advance can be made in one or more of these problems if a carefully selected group of scientists work on it together for a summer."[49]

The group had some early wins that summer, including in checkers, and funding was greatly expanded around the world through the early 1970s, but the pace of innovation didn't match the visionaries' expectations, and funding in the US and Britain was cut off, creating the first AI winter. Although progress still continued in pockets, it was largely due to the increasing computational power of computers, combined with digitization, that artificial intelligence finally began a lasting resurgence in the late 1990s.

An area of specific study for many in the artificial intelligence field was investigating how our own brains work. Alan Turing himself theorized that the cortex at birth is an "unorganized machine" and through "training" becomes organized "into a universal machine or something like it."[50] If brains learn like computers, then computers can learn like brains. But was

Turing right? Do we understand by reducing probabilities? Much work from behavioural science, machine learning, and psychology suggests that the answer is yes, our brains do act like Bayesian probability machines, constantly making new predictions based on changing information from our senses and assigning probabilities to the outcomes.

What is a Bayesian probability machine? A computer that works on Bayes's theorem, named after Thomas Bayes (1702–1761). Bayes's theorem assesses the probability of an event based on prior information. My favourite example comes from Pedro Domingos's book *The Master Algorithm*. In it, Domingos imagines a person waking up on a planet one afternoon at the beginning of time and seeing the sun go down and wondering if it will come back up. Because the person has never seen the sun rise, there's no reason to believe it will or it won't. Therefore, two scenarios—one the sun rising and one where it does not—are equally likely, each with a probability of one-half. With each day that the sun rises in the morning, the probability that is assigned to it rising the next day increases but never reaches 100 percent confidence, since the person could never be completely certain. Now imagine, instead of a random person at the beginning of time, that you're teleported to a strange planet at night after living on Earth. In other words, you have previous knowledge. You see stars in the sky and you know how solar systems work, so with your prior knowledge of what happens on Earth, you might start your probability that the sun will rise in the morning at two-thirds instead of 50 percent and update from there.

Through this Bayesian method, you could imagine learning any problem as long as you had a starting probability and enough cycles to update the probabilities. Similarly, a computer could solve any problem if it had a prior probability and enough data and compute power to continually adjust that probability—in other words, error correction and refinement of hypothesis through iterations. Intelligence.

Let's test this by looking at the game of Go, the oldest board game in the world. Invented in China more than 2,500 years ago, the game still has a large following of twenty million active players and professional leagues. The game is said to have up to 10^{780} playing positions—that is, a number of playing positions so large that it would be written as a 1 with 780 zeros following it. Until 2014, even top AI researchers believed top human competitors would beat computers for years to come because of the complexity of the game and the fact that algorithms had to compare every move, which required enormous compute power. But in 2016, Google's DeepMind program AlphaGo beat one of the top players in the world, Lee Sedol, in a match that made history. AlphaGo's program was based on deep learning, which was "trained" using thousands of human amateur and professional games. It made history not only because it was the first time a computer beat a top Go master, but also because of the way it did so. In game 2 and the thirty-seventh move, the computer made a move that defied logic, placing a black stone in the middle of an open area—away from the other stones. Top players in the world commentating first dismissed the move as a mistake by the AI, but then realized it was no mistake. The move was brilliant, and AlphaGo went on to beat Sedol in the game and win the five-game match 4–1. Later, pundits would say how creative the move was. It was the first time that an AI was ever said to be creative, a domain always thought to be owned solely by humans. Just one year later, in 2017, Google launched a newer version called AlphaGo Zero that beat AlphaGo 100 games to zero.

Not only was that version much more powerful than its predecessor, It also didn't require any "training" from human games. Understanding only the rules of the game, AlphaGo Zero became its own teacher, playing itself millions of times and through deep reinforcement learning getting stronger with each game. No longer constrained by human knowledge, it took only three days of the computer playing itself to best previous AlphaGo versions developed by top researchers and it continued to improve from there. It mastered the masters, then mastered itself, and kept on going.

How does this relate to our own intelligence? Geoffrey Hinton has long been trying to understand how our brains work. Hinton, the "godfather of deep learning," is a cognitive psychologist and computer scientist who moved to Canada because of its continued research funding through the second AI winter in the early 1990s. He currently divides his time between his work at Google and as a professor at the University of Toronto. He previously set up the Gatsby Computational Neuroscience Unit at University College London with the aim of "building neurobiologically realistic and computationally sound models of the way that the brain computes."[51] His work on multi-layer or artificial neural networks gave rise to a broader class of problems that machine learning could solve more effectively. That work has seen dramatic breakthroughs in many areas of machine learning.

Information and knowledge have been expanding exponentially as we build on past learnings and as we improve our technology. Soon—perhaps already—that rate of growth will be too fast for our own minds to keep pace. We will be chasing ever further behind our machines. Then who will be the masters?

7

WHO WILL BE
THE MASTERS?

WHAT MAKES A master? In a landmark 1993 study, Anders Ericsson, Ralf Krampe, and Clemens Tesch-Römer showed that the best violinists and pianists at a German music academy practiced an average of more than 10,000 hours before they turned twenty.[52] Malcolm Gladwell later looked at this in his bestseller *Outliers*, where he researched success in many fields, coming back to the magic number of 10,000 hours. Why were certain people willing to commit to practicing enough to attain mastery? Gladwell found that, in many cases, it was because of a simple human bias. They were better at it early, sometimes only because of when their birthdate fell in the calendar, making them the better part of a year older than other kids in their cohort. Because of their early success, they were reinforced positively, which then made them want to practice more.

Although the precise number of hours of dedicated practice has been disputed—some take less time, some take more, and not everyone who practices more is going to be the best in their field—the general principle makes intuitive sense: the more we practice, the better we become. Your biological computer makes predictions and corrects errors each time you practice something, and each time, the neural network of your brain alters itself to speed the connection between neurons and synapses that are important to that function. Like travelling on a superhighway instead of a back-lane gravel road, the reinforced neural pathways are able to see and react to patterns much faster than those that are not. Through more and more practice and pattern reinforcement, moves that once took energy to see are seen unconsciously.

Years ago, I remember attending an intimate event at Pebble Beach, California, where top sports and business leaders gathered to learn. One thing that struck me during the three days was how much almost every one of the elite athletes talked about practice—not the big things, but repetition of small moves. Even in that group, Jerry Rice, former wide receiver for the San Francisco 49ers, stood out, talking about practicing long after teammates had gone home and through the offseason so that he would come to each camp in the best shape of his life. That dedicated practice made Jerry Rice one of the best wide receivers of all time.

But can you imagine Jerry Rice stepping off the football field and playing piano like Elton John or understanding physics like Einstein? The repetitive practice in the brain solidifies connections at the expense of other connections. It is not that new information and new things cannot be learned, but without lattice in the brain to connect to—previous recognized patterns—learning anything completely new is difficult. Unlike the things we know well where the neural connections are strengthened, the brain has to rewire itself through repetition and error correcting. And that becomes the trap—when new thinking is needed, it is very easy for us to remain entrenched.

The power of technology

Let's look back at the game of Go. To achieve 10,000 hours of dedicated practice at Go, a human being would need to commit four hours a day, five days per week, for about ten years. In that amount of time and number of games, the human would see a lot of moves and combinations of moves but never come close to ever seeing a 1 with 780 zeros behind it. If the human made a move every six seconds—which isn't likely—10,000 hours would be six million moves. But a computer—not just a supercomputer but *any* computer that you can buy today— could play through six million moves in much less time than it would take a human to play *one* move.

Even if the human being could play that many games over the same time period as a computer, another problem exists: how we remember or recall. In a 3,000-person study published in the *Journal of Experimental Psychology*, researchers asked participants various questions about the September 11 attacks, from who they were with, to how many planes were involved, to how they felt about the attacks.[53] Large inconsistencies emerged from what people reported immediately afterwards versus what they reported later. Almost 40 percent of the time, people misremembered some aspect of their 9/11 experience.

We all misremember. As our brain consolidates information from all of our senses from short-term to long-term memory, it generalizes and looks for existing patterns to connect to new information, filling in gaps where necessary. Right now, as you read or listen to these words, your brain is taking in far more information than you could possibly remember. In addition to the words and concepts in this book, your brain is concurrently taking information from all of your senses, the smell and feeling of the air around you, the temperature, the touch, a bird singing in the distance, colours. What you remember is tied to other memories or thoughts to reinforce your own narrative. Each moment you experience something new, it is combined with previous information. Because it is impossible to store all of that information, you either subconsciously or consciously are choosing what is important and what deserves attention. Some of that information moves to your working memory, where you hold it for reasoning and decision-making.

Working memory is limited in capacity. Your working memory is generally believed to have a capacity of seven items, plus or minus two.[54] That is consistent whether it is stored in digits, letters, or other units. Here's a quick demonstration. Read the following letter/number combination: D729F58.

Now multiply 37 times 42.

Now, without looking back, try to recall the letter/number combination.

Because our senses are constantly bringing in a staggering amount of new information and the storage capacity of our brains is limited, our brains simplify what we store to only the most important parts. If information seems to match our own mental model, we encode it that way. In simplifying, some vivid details are lost or melded with other memories to create something that might not be entirely accurate. That storage uses our own filters of past experiences to remember things that look similar to what the brain associates with the new memories.

Perhaps this is the same reason that it takes dedicated practice to achieve superior results. The practice corrects previous errors until mastery is attained. More and more practice enables moves that you know are correct to be wired into the brain so they are made unconsciously. Patterns can be seen without knowing that you're seeing them. Because those patterns are now committed to your unconscious, conscious energy is freed up for more important moves or decisions, as any elite athlete and many others will tell you about a state of flow.

Another way the brain seems to encode information more quickly is through the deemed importance of the information—how it stands out versus all other information. A strong example of that type of memory is the birth of a child or the death of a loved one. The more vivid and emotional the experience, the more easily it seems to encode into the brain—but again, not necessarily correctly or in ways that help us. The world that we each see and therefore experience is very different from what others see and experience. Our minds look for things that match our own sense of reality and then continually build on those patterns—rarely questioning their validity or value. We don't actually hear or perceive what others "say" in the way they mean it; rather, we "hear" them through our own filters of previous information encoding.

Computers are not bound by that thinking.

Computers do not attach emotion to storage of information in the way that humans do. They do not have a bias problem (unless programmed in by a human). They recall data exactly as received. With enough data or rules of a game, computers can see all combinations and their impact on each other, instead of a seeing only the small sampling that a human can. But what seems like superhuman intelligence is just pattern recognition and error correction at scale, without the shortcuts humans need to compensate for efficiency. With enough data and compute power, a computer can play billions of simulations concurrently and learn from every one of them, all without forgetting mistakes made in previous games. And once it has learned, it never gets tired and it never forgets.

It is not therefore a difficult leap for the imagination that—with enough data, compute power, and storage—almost any problem that could be solved by a human could be better solved by a computer.

What's coming

As artificial intelligence moves across industries, the gains to humanity are incredible. But as each new skill is acquired by artificial intelligence, jobs are at risk since AI will do them better at a drastically different price. With each new skill learned by computers, more knowledge is added to the knowledge graph of the world and that skill can be applied anywhere at almost no cost. That creates an even faster rate of innovation where artificial intelligence becomes superior to human intelligence across all fields.

Many will be skeptical of that prediction because, as it stands, humans are far better at generalizing than computers— better at taking a pattern from one domain into another. Human beings, for now, are still vastly superior to computers in applying learning from various different fields as analogues to new fields. The computer program that beat Lee Sedol at Go cannot drive a car, and the one that drives a car cannot win at *Jeopardy!* Today's machine learning consists of narrow AI.

But if narrow AI could beat humans in those specific domains as long as they had enough information, what if a narrow AI was built in every field? Could enough narrow AIs be strung together to render many of the things that we consider special about ourselves not so special at all? In fact, isn't that the way that our jobs and economies are built today? Our own specialized knowledge is what we are paid for in our careers, with top dollars going to the "best" or "experts" in specialized domains. In business, sports, music, and just about any other field, the top people make tens to hundreds of times as much money as the average person. That race to be the best drives competition and learning, which in itself is often the motivating force driving the long years of dedicated practice to attain mastery. But as computers reign supreme in any given field, the monetary incentive for humans to be the best also falls. Why dedicate your entire life trying to master something that AI can do routinely with far better outcomes? If AlphaGo Zero takes only three days to beat all human competitors and then keeps getting better from there, does being a Go champion lose its status?

Don't forget how rapidly this is accelerating now. The first *Homo sapiens* emerged over 300,000 years ago. The alphabet, which enabled writing, was invented approximately 3,000 years ago. The printing press was invented almost 600 years ago. The first mechanical computer was envisioned (not built) 170 years ago. The first ideas around artificial intelligence were developed seventy years ago. The first AI to beat a grandmaster in chess was developed twenty-three years ago. The first AI to beat *Jeopardy!* was eight years ago. The first to beat a grandmaster at Go was three years ago. The growth of AI is now being measured in months or days, instead of years, decades, or even centuries. Tomorrow it will be measured in minutes and seconds.

The key point—the difference between man and machine is that in combinatorial problems—where there is too much information for humans to see or act on—computers with deep learning algorithms have a massive advantage. Yes, early on the AIs will make mistakes, like humans do today, but the errors will be corrected at a rate that humans cannot fathom.

Every platform uses narrow artificial intelligence to solve problems in a way similar to AlphaGo Zero, and that's what makes them so valuable for users. Amazon would never be able to choose which of their 500 million products to display in front of each unique person without AI. Google sorts trillions of web pages available using similar AI. It's how you get the app you want out of the millions available in the store, and how YouTube serves you up videos you might be interested in. What's next?

How about your health?

The body digitized

Your body and what affects it—from its genetic makeup, to your environment, to the food you eat, to your gut biome, to your exercise patterns, and much more—can be looked at as information and digitized. The variety of informational inputs has too many combinatorial outcomes for the human mind to understand properly. Because humans can't see all the moving parts—there are far too many—we are forced to generalize, and therefore we miss important clues. Look at the way drugs are brought to market today. Billions of dollars are spent on research and trials. Many of these drugs demonstrate unintended consequences in wider trials, or after they've been approved: the interaction between human and drug is different because each of us is different.

How different? Take your genome by way of example. The entire human genome—our complete set of DNA—was sequenced for the first time in 2003. It contains approximately three billion base pairs of two of four possible chemical units; they reside in the twenty-three pairs of chromosomes within the nucleus of all our cells. Each chromosome contains hundreds to thousands of genes, which carry the instructions for making proteins. You could think of your genome as an instruction booklet for how to make and operate a human. But it's an enormous instruction booklet, one you could never fully understand because of its complexity. There are more possible combinations, and interactions between combinations, than a human mind can understand, and that complexity is only magnified by other inputs like exercise, environment, food, and drugs we take. It's like the game of Go: how many of the "moves" do we and our health practitioners not see because we are only capable of seeing a small portion of the overall "moves" and reinforcing the patterns we have learned?

Do you have an Apple Watch? If you do, you have an example of the future of healthcare on your wrist. Apple's watch already collects heart rate information, ECG information, exercise patterns, and sleep patterns. By detecting heart rate abnormalities or elevation in heart rates, it has already saved many lives. Beyond your heart data, it also collects information on your sleep and exercise patterns, which in turn could be used to promote health. Health data—from your genome to your Apple Watch data and even your Google searches— is the start of creating digital engines that could give rise to artificial intelligence making the same leaps in health as we have seen in many other domains. The many different inputs help to ensure a constant stream of important data that drives the artificial intelligence faster, which in turn drives far better outcomes in health, which in turn drives more data. The data collection we have today is not sufficient to dramatically change healthcare. But it is already collecting far more real-time data than my doctor has.

Imagine if Apple provided a service to digitize my DNA so that they could combine it with my fitness, sleep, and other data. If I trusted the privacy of their network, I might willingly sign over my data to the company because of the potential benefits that it could provide. With their additional data and feedback loop to my better health outcomes, after I provided that data, I might add my health records and medicines I take. Each time this gives access for AI to process all of the data together, which could yield extraordinary benefits that accrete to me in the form of health outcomes, all through a unified health platform.

These new platforms in health are likely to be monopolies—like the others we see today—for the same reasons. The benefit to users is too big to ignore and the consolidation of information makes the benefit increasingly better. The only question is: will that data monopoly be owned by Google, Amazon, or Apple, or one of the other platforms that is already moving quickly into the space, or by a new upstart that has sufficient resources to expand its data capture quickly? Again, like free search on Google, the network effects and data advantage will provide benefits that are incredible for society. This will be great news for our health outcomes, cost of medicine, and a few select companies that are able to consolidate vast information.

It will also, again, be bad news for jobs. Why? Look at how many jobs come from waste in the system caused by information asymmetry. Think of a case where you go to multiple doctors—family doctor, radiologist, gastroenterologist, other specialists—who each have their own staff and each only have a part of your information. As you are treated, repetitive trips, further specialization, and often misdiagnoses are all part of the overall health budget. When artificial intelligence reduces that waste and increases the benefits to society, as a by-product of removing the waste in the system, it reduces the number of jobs in healthcare. With more than $3.5 trillion of annual spending and 19 percent of the US GDP in healthcare, that could mean a lot of jobs.

For instance, as reported in a May 2019 *Nature Medicine* article, researchers created a 3D volumetric deep learning model to screen for lung cancer.[55] When comparing a single image, the deep learning model outperformed six radiology experts, with an 11 percent reduction in false positives and a 5 percent reduction in false negatives. According to Dr. Mozziyar Etemadi, one of the study's coauthors, "AI in 3D can be much more sensitive in its ability to detect early lung cancer than the human eye looking at 2D images. This is technically '4D' because it is not only looking at one CT scan but two (the current and prior scan) over time." And if the current reality of AI in lung cancer detection is already beating the experts, how much better will it be next year, or the year after that, with significantly more data and error correction? The technology has the potential to save a lot of lives in early detection. It also has the potential to cost a lot of radiologists their jobs.

Ask yourself: Would you choose the cheaper, more effective option or the one that costed more but protected jobs if your or your family's health was on the line?

It is true that, in many early examples, artificial intelligence performs better when combined with humans instead of on its own. The first version of AlphaGo that took years to develop by mirroring actual games and through the work of many AI researchers serves as an example. That fact leads some people to extrapolate scenarios where we work together with AI and there is an abundance of jobs. While I agree with the prognosis that in the short term humans are needed to help train and error correct artificial intelligence, it does not appear to me that this is any more than a transition step. We will error correct the machines until they are more "intelligent" than us. So for a short term, there might be more jobs, but then those "training the AI" jobs fall away as AI takes knowledge to the next level. Remember that just a year after AlphaGo's release, AlphaGo Zero came out, not needing people, and winning 100 games to zero. It's a potent example of what is possible.

The AI race

But it's not just about increases in compute power. We are at an inflection point where it is about gathering the right data in data sets that can be analyzed by machines and then helping train those data sets. All of today's top companies globally are data companies that enjoy network effects, capturing more data as they grow, which in turn creates better systems. They are creating data monopolies where vast data sets are being combined to produce impressive results. The more data, and the more data velocity, the better the artificial intelligence becomes and the better outcomes from it. Top researchers in AI are attracted to companies that have these data sets because of the faster rate of experimenting. As the holders of our data amass giant data sets, they ultimately control the world.

That is the real race today, a race that is geopolitical in scope and scale. Look no further than Vladimir Putin's comment about artificial intelligence in 2017: "Whoever becomes the leader in this sphere will become the ruler of the world."[56] It is not only companies but countries that are investing heavily to win this race.

That race for AI superiority may be behind some recent high-profile events between governments. The Huawei case, where the United States government charged China's Huawei and its officers of intellectual property theft as well as sanctions violations, offers clues to that race. It is no secret that Huawei has ambitions to build an infrastructure backbone to capture data flows. Its own tagline, "Building a fully connected, intelligent world," captures it succinctly. Powering much of the 5G network that will allow faster communications would give any company, including Huawei, a tremendous advantage in data capture. The real revolution of 5G is not only the twenty times speed advantage over 4G networks prevalent today but the amount of data that can be transmitted through the increased bandwidth.

Although there may be truth to the allegations by the United States, a secondary reason for the high-stakes play could be to slow down a competitor. A well-worn strategy used in business is to sue a competitor to put them on the defence and subsequently slow them down while the competing business in parallel develops a plan to win a key market. Irrespective of the actual facts of the case or the implications, if Huawei was deemed to be in a leadership position in a key market that the US saw as strategic, a move like this would make sense.

China itself may have a unique advantage in the artificial intelligence race because of the size of its population and its state control, which could allow data collection at a faster rate. The government could decide to collect and monitor data sets, and citizens would have little say because, unlike democratic countries that need to get voters aligned with large changes that could potentially violate human rights, the government can roll out sweeping changes without asking for permission. One such example is China's social credit system. Designed by the State Council in 2014, the idea would "allow the trust-worthy to roam everywhere under heaven while making it hard for the discredited to take a single step."

The system works as follows: all of China's population receives a score that is available as public record. Points are deducted for things like traffic violations, bad debt, or selling faulty products, and points are added for giving to charity, giving blood, or other good deeds. The idea behind the original plan might not seem bad at a high level; it was targeting dishonesty in government affairs and encouraging commercial and social integrity. But it is easy to see where such a system could be open to error and manipulation. The rules of the systems are not universal, and the systems are not interconnected. In some regions, listening to music too loudly deducts points; in others, jaywalking or playing video games does. It would be hard to imagine any system in China that rewarded opposition in any form to the Communist Party. The system is already functioning in twelve regions and is set to roll out countrywide in 2020. By the end of 2018 in the twelve regions, the system had already blocked access for 5.4 million people from travelling on high speed trains and an additional 17 million people from taking airline flights.

Once established, it is easy to see how a digital surveillance system owned by a government and driven by artificial intelligence could gain tremendous power and leverage over its citizens. The addition of other data sets could be mandated quickly. Messaging apps, website visits, facial recognition, medical data, and other forms of interactions could be stitched together to provide absolute control in Orwellian fashion. If the machines are controlling the population, who is controlling the machines? The control of the data driving the artificial intelligence could easily lead to a different kind of power that is almost absolute in nature. As the old saying by British historian Lord Acton goes, "Power tends to corrupt, and absolute power corrupts absolutely."[57]

While in the United States it might be easy to call for a breakup of monopoly power that currently resides in technology companies like Google or Amazon, doing so might actually create worse outcomes. In a race for AI superiority that is geopolitical in nature, the slowing of any US corporations' artificial intelligence aspirations due to regulation might, at the same time, cede control of AI superiority to foreign governments, like China or Russia.

Ben Goertzel and many others want a different future for AI. Ben believes that there is high risk if AI is controlled by a corporation or government. Goals for an organization or government may be very different than that of a population. If AI is owned by corporations or governments, then the benefits will accrue to very few. He has long advocated that artificial general intelligences have the potential to be massively more ethical and compassionate than humans. But still, the odds of getting deeply beneficial AGIs seem higher if the humans creating them are fuller of compassion and positive consciousness. His company, SingularityNET, aims to decentralize AI and open the benefits to everyone. I've been lucky enough to spend some time talking over beers with Ben and I share this view about the downside of having any corporation or government with as much control over something that will become so powerful. So do many others, including Elon Musk and Reid Hoffman, who helped kick off the OpenAI initiative. OpenAI's mission is to "build safe AGI and ensure AGI's benefits are as widely and evenly distributed as possible."

But although these open initiatives are laudable, what hurts many of them is the lack of data and data velocity, which inhibits the learning rate. Core to every one of the major platforms is a product or service that compels you to give them your data for free—from your Google searches, to your Alexa enquiries, to your Instagram pictures. The platform then monetizes your data in numerous ways, selling products or services more effectively to you or selling your data to advertisers. All the while the platform is using its tremendous data advantage to make its service better and better. Providing your data seems like a small price to pay for the extraordinary benefit of the service. That in itself becomes the problem with open AI initiatives outside of companies where there is a financial incentive to give away a product or service to get the data to make the product better. It is hard to see any of these open initiatives gaining enough momentum without an extraordinary product or service that is core to their data capture. Without that "hook" for users, data capture slows, or data becomes significantly more expensive, which reinforces itself, resulting in a suboptimal experience that drives users to something better—likely a commercial enterprise.

Underlying our intelligence as a species always has been, and still is, fundamentally a collective growth of information. It's not to say that all of the information was right throughout history. There has been, and there still is today, a lot of misinformation. Error correcting on our information gave rise to a world of science and discovery that led to many of the advances we take for granted today, with each cycle feeding back on itself to give rise to an exponential gain in more information and knowledge. It is logical that the flood of information and knowledge is now transferred to computers because of their ability to "see" and correct patterns in massive data sets better and faster than we can. That rate of growth will soon mean that humanity's reign at the top of the "intelligence" pyramid will fall. As Geordie Rose, cofounder of D-Wave Systems, one of the top quantum computer companies, said to me a couple of summers ago, is any human's job secure—present or future—if you could instead hire the android, Data, from *Star Trek*?

This also leads to a logical next step in our own evolution.

I, for one, do not worry about artificial intelligence taking over the world one day. It is not that there aren't risks along the way from misuse or misunderstanding of the new intelligence superpowers. Those risks include some laid out already—like a single country or company dominating artificial intelligence that leaves few people controlling a vast power and the rest of humanity as pawns to that power. But a higher probability is that we extend our brains. Just as books were an extension of our minds that gave us tremendous rise in "intelligence" and the ability to better master our world, the next logical step might be the integration of mind and machine. Research is quickly expanding on brain–computer interfaces, and many people would readily choose a path that would exponentially increase their own "intelligence." As Elon Musk recently said about robots, "If you can't beat them, join them."[58]

But whether we embrace it or not, the genie will not be put back in the bottle. These things are true: 1) error correction is at the heart of all of our "intelligence"; 2) information is growing at an exponential pace; 3) that information is being transferred to computers that can gain knowledge and correct errors faster than human brains can; and 4) Every one of our jobs is a function of our intelligence.

If every job is a function of our intelligence, as computers beat us at intelligence, how could any job be safe? These facts lead to very predictable social disruption because our entire economies are designed around jobs and far fewer will be needed to run our societies. This will lead to an inevitable rise of division and polarization if we continue to mask the fundamental issue. Can we—with our machines—learn how to solve it in time? Can we step forward and accept a new era of abundance?

8

US VERSUS THEM

"I COULDN'T BELIEVE HOW fast people changed."

Alex Mocevic grew up in a comfortable middle-class home in Sarajevo, in the former state of Yugoslavia. In 1984 Sarajevo hosted the Winter Olympics. A decade later it was a bombed-out war zone, and Alex escaped to Canada with nothing but the clothes on his back and no ability to speak English.

I got to know Alex in Canada a number of years later when he came to work with me, and we quickly became friends. He told me about his childhood: his parents had had good jobs, good benefits, and a very good quality of life. Alex was Bosnian Christian Orthodox and he had friends across different religious groups. Kids played in the streets. To Alex, life was amazing. And then, as he told me, "That changed almost overnight."

Religion was used to divide. Him from his friends, his friends from him. At the outset of the war in 1992, Alex's family believed that if they didn't take sides and stayed in their home, they would be safe. In an instant, Alex was living on the wrong side of a border, trapped one day in his home with his family on the other side of the frontier. Attempting to leave risked being shot from both sides: from one because you were trying to escape, and from the other because you were mistaken for an attacker. The people who controlled his area would come in and search homes, randomly taking people to torture or kill them while stealing all their valuables. Alex's grandparents lived eighteen kilometres from the city and he watched their entire village burn one evening from his upper floor window.

Alex was one of the lucky ones. The first and last UN convoy evacuated him along with some other children six months later. He lived in a refugee camp for more than three of the next years—"a war zone of its own." Not welcome in his birth country, he was finally granted asylum in Canada after many applications. He did not have any communication with his parents, grandparents, or the rest of his family for years. His parents lived through that time thanks to various people who hid them from the authorities. Eventually his mom was allowed a day reprieve because the authorities figured that, with a husband on the other side, she would return. With the rest of his family safe, Alex's father made his own daring escape during a late-night run across the border.

Imagine that happening where you live. Don't think it couldn't.

What is it about human beings that allows us to become influenced so quickly? We are all born without prejudice, hate, or division, so how does it get there?

Belonging—and exclusion

All species form some sort of groups. The biological significance or importance cannot be understated, originating likely from a need for survival of a species. The lack of an ability to form bonds is associated with some of the most severe personality disorders, such as paranoia and schizophrenia, and much research has been done on the need for humans to belong. In a 1995 research paper, Roy Baumeister and Mark Leary maintain that there is an almost universal need for humans to bond, and that it has a major impact on happiness and on social, emotional, and physical well-being. "The need to belong is a powerful, fundamental, and extremely pervasive motivation," they write, and they discuss the possibility that "much of what human beings do is done in the service of belongingness."[59]

It's hard to underestimate the importance of this in our everyday lives, with many of the things we choose to do ultimately servicing this need. Our need to form strong bonds or relationships touches just about everything we see. It is responsible for many of our actions—whether we know it or not. These social interactions are foundational in driving human society and form the basis of our family, friends, political institutions, and global economy.

The science of social psychology studies how our thoughts, feelings, beliefs, intentions, and behaviours are influenced and in turn influence our interactions with others. Many of us think that we are in total control of our thoughts, but we fail to understand that our thoughts are highly influenced by the people around us and everything we read, see, and do. Many of those same choices are because we want to belong. That influence on us, much of which we don't realize, traps us in our own bubble of reality that may look very different than others'.

Belonging to one group most likely also means not belonging to another group. As a consequence, a natural by-product of deepening some relationships is not deepening others—or worse. This can create "us versus them," and it is a far more powerful force in your life than you may realize.

Think about all the groups you belong to. There are hundreds or even thousands of them. It could be anything, from your friends' group in college to a nation that you are proud to call home. They do not need to be formal. Often, the groups are labels that you proudly wear—hoping to be reinforced by belonging. Here are some of the groups and identities that I unofficially belong to: entrepreneur, YPO member, Canadian, optimist, family man, empath, skier, tennis player, volleyball player, hockey player, hiker, camper, friend, visionary, intellectually curious person, introvert. Every one of those labels (and many more) brings opportunities to share an identity with like-minded people. I naturally do more things to reinforce the groups that I belong to and associate with people who share my interests.

These differentiations in our minds are often about being not only different but *better* in some way. Those groups make us stand out by saying, "I'm like this, those people are like that" or "You and I are like this, those people are like that." "Here is why you and I belong, why we understand each other" also implies "Here is why those others don't, can't, or never will understand us." Consider for a moment just one of the individual groups or identities that you belong to and all the positive effects of belonging to that group. Are you an optimist or a pessimist? Hero or victim? Do you design for belongingness and validation through your progression in your career or how much money you have, or in spite of it? Which sports team do you cheer for? You would not associate with that group if it were not for the positive feelings you gain from it. Now consider the competition with other groups, and whether that competition is good-natured. Without realizing, we can easily fall into a trap of believing that we are somehow better than others outside of our group.

It happens with every one of our labels—race, religion, income level, education, politics, whatever it may be. How many minutes has it been since you last categorized someone? You may even be doing it right now during the reading of this book: you and I are aligned in thinking or we're not—creating either a closer connection between us or driving a wedge. It is a natural tendency, needing to assign people to a group—yours or otherwise. How about when you've been travelling? Have you met someone who turned out to be from your hometown or country? It often seems easier to connect with someone from your hometown in a faraway country than it is in your hometown. There is an immediate connection of belonging, of something in common that sets you apart. Building these bonds seems to be hardwired into us ... and that means that the unintended consequences of building the bonds— that it divides us from others—might be hardwired as well.

In a famous set of social psychology experiments done in the 1950s through early 1960s, Muzafer Sherif (1906–1988) focused on intergroup conflict and resolution between eleven- and twelve-year-old white protestant boys of similar social economic upbringing. The experiment was called the Robbers Cave experiment. None of the boys knew that they were participants in a study. Sherif set out by randomly assigning the boys to one of two groups and put them in different parts of a camp so they could each create a common group identity. Each group named itself—for example, the Eagles and the Rattlers—and made flags celebrating the individuality of their own groups. Once group identity was established, Sherif went on to the next phase of the experiment by setting up competition for scarce resources, in this case pocket knives and other prizes that the boys highly valued, with no prizes given to the losers. This part of the experiment lasted between four and six days and set the stage for conflict between the groups.

Over the course of competition, the groups became increasingly hostile to each other. What started as good sportsmanship escalated to quickly to name calling, cheating, raiding of cabins, and fistfights. Some of the boys carried around rocks in their socks as protection in case they were ambushed by the other team. As Sherif noted in his 1966 book *Group Conflict and Cooperation*, competition generally led to "us versus them" group identities. Through this experiment, boys with no behavioural issues were turned into hostile, narrow-minded opponents.[60]

For the purpose of this book, the most important part of Sherif's research was in phases three and four of the experiments: once they were locked into their respective groups, Sherif attempted to bring them together. In phase three, he brought the groups together for limited times to watch movies and eat together. He hypothesized that contact alone would not have any marked decrease in the tension between groups. This was confirmed in all contact sessions, with teams either sitting separately, calling names, or in one case having a food fight at dinner. In phase four of the experiment, Sherif introduced superordinate goals—higher-level goals where he believed that groups would come together to solve bigger problems and move beyond their differences.

The first of these superordinate goals was the drinking water problem. In orientation, the researchers told both groups that occasionally vandals broke their only reservoir of water, so they should make sure to fill up their canteens each day. In phase four, the researchers created a problem by damaging the main source of water and announcing a water emergency to both groups that required immediate help. Both groups volunteered to help with a common goal of securing water. The water tank was located just over a mile from the camp, and after searching for damage across the entire line, the boys congregated at the tank. They found the tank three-quarters full of water and eventually found that the problem was at the valve, eventually fixing the water and saving the day. With each subsequent superordinate goal—where the groups had to work together to solve problems—the groups became closer to each other, eventually forming close relationships. As a defining moment of bringing the boys back together, on the bus ride home—just before a refreshment stop—one of the Rattlers noted that each member of their team was still owed their $5 prize for winning the beanbag toss from earlier at camp. The Rattlers, instead of spending it on themselves alone, suggested that they buy malted milks for all of the boys in both groups.

We see this dynamic playing out across our lives—sometimes even in our most important relationships. It is not isolated to eleven- and twelve-year-old boys. Ironically, because of our strong desire to belong, it is easy to divide us. Maybe, though, the Robbers Cave experiment shows us a path forward where, through the right incentives or world challenges, we can do better.

Knowing that our collective need to create strong bonds also has the potential to divide us, we must remain vigilant to its allure.

We must also be aware of the cognitive biases that feed into it. In chapter 3, we discussed how our brains evolve biases to simplify information so we can deal with it more easily. These biases include the halo effect, where our overall impression of someone is driven by something concrete, like assuming intelligence based on good looks; the in-group bias, where we tend to favour members of our own groups; and the out-group homogeneity bias, where we believe people in other groups all act the same while our group is more diverse. And while it is easy to read these once and move on, we all are subject to them, which means that the stories that we live and tell ourselves are largely based on how we have encoded our previous experiences, which might not be about the facts but how we have interpreted them.

Taken together, that means that we may easily be manipulated, and worse, that manipulation can reinforce itself and lead us to believe it was our idea in the first place.

With a greater understanding of social persuasion and how it affects all of us, I have been increasingly fascinated with what thoughts are truly my own and which ones have been implanted there by others. One of my long-time favourite quotes is the following by Frank Outlaw, from 1977. Most of our time is spent within our own heads, so it makes sense that how we interpret our thoughts leads to many of the other things that we experience:

> Watch your thoughts, they become words;
> watch your words, they become actions;
> watch your actions, they become habits;
> watch your habits, they become character;
> watch your character, for it becomes your destiny.[61]

The power of understanding needs and desires

The ability to connect with our deepest human needs is something that drives immense influence and power. You might be able to see it in your personal relationships, where deeper and broader social networks create significant influence. But you might miss that every leader, company, brand, and political institution uses a similar understanding to build power. In itself that is neither good nor bad. Throughout history, the greatest leaders, brands, companies, and institutions have used that influence and persuasion to make our world better. Inspirational leaders like Martin Luther King Jr., Mohandas Gandhi, Abraham Lincoln, and Nelson Mandela come to mind in their efforts to make our world better and more just. And even if you do not agree with everything Elon Musk does or says, it is hard to argue that he has not mastered the ability to influence and, because of that influence, has accelerated numerous industries for the betterment of humanity.

With so much to be gained, understanding how humans make decisions and how to influence those decisions is central to power: gaining it and keeping it. In 1943, American psychologist Abraham Maslow (1908–1970) proposed a theory that all humans possess a hierarchy of needs from basic need to self-actualization: some needs were more important than others, and needs on one level must be satisfied before the next can be addressed.[62] As an example, survival is a basic need and, as a result, is the first thing that motivates our behaviour. If you are starving, it is difficult to think about other needs.

Maslow's Hierarchy of Human Needs

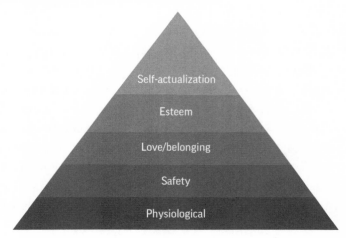

One of the early criticisms of Maslow's pyramid was that there was not enough scientific rigour to back it up. In 2011, Louis Tay and Ed Diener released a study to test his theory. According to Tay and Diener, "The findings suggest that Maslow's theory is largely correct. In cultures all over the world the fulfillment of his proposed needs correlates with happiness."[63]

It is worth considering where others are on Maslow's framework as compared to where you are. It is easy to apply your perspective on how other people "should" act when they are on a different level, instead of asking the question, "How would I act?" If you or your family were dying of starvation, or being persecuted, what would you do differently from what you're doing now?

Understanding needs and desires and then targeting them is at the heart of persuasion, so it's no surprise that this early work by Maslow helped propel marketing and communications in countless industries and brands. It's not the only psychological insight that has. The work of researchers at the front lines of behaviour science is underlying most of our products and services. Advertising and marketing deliberately play on our desires and biases to guide our thoughts. Core to every product, service, or organization is influencing your decisions. We may not even realize how we came to believe something in the first place. Ask most people why they believe, for example, that Tide is a better detergent than others, and they will have, in their minds, a logical reason for their choice but be unaware of how marketing played a role in shaping that opinion.

If beliefs on things as trivial as detergent can be molded without our knowledge or consent, what else can?

With that in mind, it's no surprise that there's been an explosion of research in the last decade into how to tap our deepest desires. It has been helped by technological advancements in brain scanning techniques; researchers can pinpoint precisely what areas of the brain are reacting and why. Understanding why we do things, even when we might not realize ourselves, and shaping that behaviour is what advertising, influence, and power is about.

In his seminal book *Actionable Gamification*, Yu-kai Chou proposes a framework called Octalysis. In that framework, Yu-kai believes that there are eight motivational forces that drive every action we take—not just in games, but foundational to everything. He believes that they can be built into a framework that can be used to massively influence us because our brains are hardwired to accept these motivational forces:

1. Epic Meaning and Calling—The idea that you are doing something greater than yourself or the belief that you were chosen to do something.

2. Development and Accomplishment—The internal drive of making progress, developing skills, and eventually overcoming meaningful challenges.

3. Creativity and Feedback—When you are engaged in a creative process where you have to repeatedly figure things out and try different combinations of actions to progress.

4. Ownership and Possession—The feeling of owning something: wealth, properties, data, collectables...

5. Social Pressure and Relatedness—All the social elements that drive people, including mentorship, acceptance, social responses, companionship, as well as competition and envy.

6. Scarcity and Impatience—Wanting something because you can't have it, because the resource is scarce or because you are prevented from accessing it.

7. Unpredictability and Curiosity—Wanting to find out what will happen next—such as when watching a movie or while gambling.

8. Loss and Avoidance—The avoidance of something negative happening.[64]

If Yu-kai is right, the framework can allow anyone to reverse engineer user behaviour to satisfy almost any objective, trivial or otherwise.

A simple example of game mechanics shows this power to get you addicted. A digital game is something that you choose to play. You spend your time without any chance of monetary reward. That precious time could be spent on countless activities that would yield greater benefit for you. And while you might believe that you spend the time on the game because of your own desire, let's explore what drives that desire from a game designer's perspective.

What mechanisms in game design create habits and keep us coming back? For example, if a game is too difficult to win early, users get frustrated and do not stick with it, so game designers include early wins or prizes to create dopamine responses in your brains, which create stickiness. As the game progresses, if it is too easy to win or collect prizes, users quickly get bored and drop off. Over time, by increasing the difficulty in combination with giving ownership of prizes that can be used to get through harder levels, game designers create a ladder of motivators to keep your brain engaged. Leaving the game after collecting rewards that make you better at the game feels like a loss—and triggers you to keep coming back. It takes using the right balance of motivators at the right time to get and keep your attention.

It's no surprise, then, that many of the top companies in the world are using Octalysis, or a similar framework, because it works so effectively. It is everywhere from the red number on your device's app icon telling you that you have a waiting notification (that needs to be clicked to be removed) to the design of popular products like Facebook or Fortnite. It creates persuasion and addiction that we might not even question—believing our actions are derived from our own free will.

I've personally worked with Yu-kai, his team, and the Octalysis framework in a number of the companies where I am involved, and he has worked with top companies such as eBay and Google. After practicing the framework and seeing the results, I have come to realize the importance of this work in a much broader sense.

Our world does not look like it did ten or twenty years ago. The more recent knowledge of how our brains work (and how we make decisions) combined with the technology to target individuals ensures that we all see different results online. It's easy to understand the benefit for an organization to target me with things that I will click on: higher conversion and revenue, which many of the algorithms driving the results sets are designed to achieve. But there is a benefit for me, too. As those results are narrowed, my time is more effective because I do not need to endlessly search; artificial intelligence has already determined that I will not click on them. As I click or do not click, the results are further narrowed, and with each action I take, it learns what I want and that improves and guides what is right for me. The narrowing of the trillions of web pages on Google to a small number that I see is not a bug in the system—it is a feature.

We know that our thoughts and actions are highly influenced by what we see, read, and listen to, so that means that the technology that targets us naturally creates filter bubbles. We might not even realize where an idea was implanted in our brains in the first place. As we click on the things we like, these bubbles reinforce on themselves—deepening the connections in our brains and hardening our views. We rarely look outside our own bubble of reality; and when we do, the people in other filter bubbles look downright crazy. It could be religion, politics, economics, race, or any number of other divisions.

The conjunction of those three things—1) Maslow's hierarchy, where many in the world or even our own backyard are at very different stages of the pyramid; 2) technology that targets us individually and therefore reinforces belief patterns; and 3) a natural tendency in humans to create "us versus them"— has the potential to create a dangerous reinforcing loop where hate and division reign.

Especially if the world is becoming more unequal.

The rise of extremism

All these factors are at the root of the rising extremism globally. It is driven by inequality and loss of hope that come from economic disparities. People do not naturally hate others when they're content or have abundance. They are manipulated into it when they feel discounted or that they have nothing to lose. When any group is experiencing what they believe is unjust, it is easy to consolidate power from that same disillusionment. As in the Robbers Cave experiment, escalation of conflict comes from competing for scarce resources, but the escalation of conflict in this real-life experiment is for high-paying jobs. Because it is easy to take advantage of the need to belong, more often than not, the way to consolidate power is through presenting others as villains causing our suffering.

A classic example is Adolf Hitler's rise to power in Germany after World War I. The years following World War I were harsh for the German people. Humiliating defeat in the war and resentment of the Treaty of Versailles combined with food shortages, high unemployment rates, and trade tariffs designed to protect other countries like the United States from losing jobs to Germany all fuelled discontent. To drive employment and the economy, the government added enormous amounts of debt that could then not be repaid. Germany began printing large amounts of money, which caused hyperinflation, wiping out all debt—and all savings. One US dollar in 1914 was equal to 4 German marks; by 1923, the same US dollar was worth 4.2 trillion German marks. Imagine a life's savings not being enough to purchase a loaf of bread. As leader of the National Socialist German Workers' Party, or Nazi Party, Hitler used this growing frustration to build a strong following. He made a failed early attempt at revolution with his Munich Beer Hall Putsch and was imprisoned in 1923; while imprisoned, in an effort to continue his "us versus them" narrative, Hitler wrote *Mein Kampf* (*My Struggle*), originally titled *Four and a Half Years (of Struggle) against Lies, Stupidity and Cowardice.*

In 1924, together with the Dawes Plan, in which US banks lent against German institutional assets, a new currency was established that brought some stability back to the German economy and, with it, stability in government. But in 1929, the US financial collapse and subsequent depression caused the US banks to call their loans to Germany. Unable to pay the loans, Germany again faced massive unemployment and instability, which Hitler used to build party membership quickly. The Nazi Party received 19 percent of the vote in 1930 and from there continued to consolidate power through propaganda until 1933, when the Enabling Act gave Hitler ultimate power and dictatorship, which he used to systematically kill an estimated six million Jews and eleven million others in concentration camps in his pursuit of an Aryan race. A master race against all others. Us versus them taken to the extreme.

Hitler was an expert in using propaganda to influence and control. In *Mein Kampf*, he wrote,

> propaganda must always address itself to the broad masses of the people [who] are not made up of diplomats or professors of public jurisprudence nor simply of persons who are able to form reasoned judgment in given cases, but a vacillating crowd of human children who are constantly wavering between one idea and another. The great majority of a nation is so feminine in its character and outlook that its thought and conduct are ruled by sentiment rather than by sober reasoning. This sentiment, however, is not complex, but simple and consistent. It is not highly differentiated but has only the negative and positive notions of love and hatred, right and wrong, truth and falsehood.

He further reasoned that "propaganda must not investigate the truth objectively and, in so far as it is favourable to the other side, present it according to the theoretical rules of justice; yet it must present only that aspect of the truth which is favourable to its own side."[65]

As we look back at one of the black scars on the history of humanity, it is worth considering that many of the people Hitler persuaded into following him were, in his own words, a vacillating crowd of human children. It is also worth considering leadership today and to what extent we might be being manipulated.

A famous Yale study on social psychology, conducted by psychologist Stanley Milgram (1933–1984) in the 1960s, attempted to measure our obedience to authority figures.[66] Milgram originally designed the experiment to try to answer the question, "Could the millions of accomplices to genocide in the concentration camps be just following orders?" His experiments showed that what we think we will do is different from what we actually will do. In the experiments, tested around the world with similar results, participants were asked to deliver higher and higher electrical shocks to learners when their answers to various questions were wrong. The learners were actors placed in another room strapped to an "electric chair," and there was no actual shock, but that was unknown to the participants. The experiment would only stop for two reasons: 1) the fake shock was delivered at its highest setting, 450 volts, and the learner was deemed "unconscious" and non-responding, or 2) the participant objected to all of the following prompts in order: 1) *Please* continue, 2) The experiment *requires* that you continue, 3) It is *absolutely essential* that you continue, and 4) You have no other choice, you *must* go on.

While every participant stopped the test at least once, objecting to the screams in the other room or to the screams falling silent, all participants delivered at least 300-volt shocks, and 65 percent of participants delivered the final 450-volt shock.

Milgram later wrote, "Ordinary people, simply doing their jobs, and without any particular hostility on their part, can become agents in a terrible destructive process. Moreover, even when the destructive effects of their work become patently clear, and they are asked to carry out actions incompatible with fundamental standards of morality, relatively few people have the resources needed to resist authority."[67]

The studies seem to indicate that once division and consolidation of one group against another take hold, it might be very difficult to stop, even when personal moral authority deems otherwise.

In a world where abundance is possible, it is a flawed system that gives rise to extreme inequality. The output of that inequality will lead to a negative feedback loop of more extremism. That tribe or group mentality will in turn give rise to leaders who, instead of uniting us, divide us further using simple "us versus them" narratives. They become believable, potentially generationally believable, with severe consequences for us all. A butterfly effect where seemingly small things gradually cascade into very big things. It has happened before and, if nothing is done, it will happen again.

But, again, the Robbers Cave study gives us insight on how we might solve for these conflicts or prevent them in the first place. Can we challenge ourselves to create a better system for the world today by, instead of solving for an individual competition, finding a number of bigger goals that we must all solve for the benefit of humanity? A system that, instead of working for narrow parts of our society that pits us against each other, works for the greater "us"?

The simple fact is that there is only one human race and all of us belong to it.

9

CAN WE COOPERATE?

You and a friend are caught for committing a crime. The time in prison for the crime is ten years. The police hold you in separate cells with no ability to talk to each other or collude on your answers. They do not have enough direct evidence to charge you with a more serious crime, but they do for a lesser crime which will have you and your friend each spending one year in jail. To convict you or your friend on the more serious crime, the police will need either your or your friend's admission that you did the crime together.

The police come into your room and tell you the following: if you confess and your friend does not, you will go free. You will spend zero years in prison and your friend will get the full ten years. If you both confess, you will each get five years in prison. You must assume that they are about to give your friend the same offer or already have. What should you do?

If you do not turn on your friend, and the friend does not turn on you, you both only do one year in jail. The best outcome. If you do not turn on your friend, and he turns on you, you get the full ten years in jail while your friend goes free, which is the worst outcome for you.

This is the prisoner's dilemma, one of the most famous examples in game theory. It is an example of a non-zero-sum game, where the actions of each player could make their combined situation better without taking from each other. Zero-sum games are different in that the gains from one person or group must equal the losses from another. An example of that is a cake being shared by ten people. If one person takes a bigger piece of the cake, the remaining nine all have equally smaller shares. The balance of trade in the world discussed in chapter 1 is another example of a zero-sum game in that if you combine all countries' trade surpluses and deficits, the world's trade balance must equal zero. For one country to export or sell, another must import or buy.

Back to the prisoner's dilemma. Understanding what your friend will do becomes paramount in making your decision. The grid opposite shows the different scenarios. If you look at the possible outcomes, you can see that the best overall situation combined is for you both not to betray the other. The total jail time in this case is equal to two years—one year each. The challenge is that although it is best for you to act together for mutual benefit, each person is incented to not choose this—either by the risk of doing ten years or the opportunity of going free. The rational choice then becomes you betraying

your friend and your friend betraying you, which delivers five
years each for a total of ten years in prison.

The Prisoner's Dilemma

	Your friend doesn't confess	Your friend confesses
You don't confess	You get 1 year Friend gets 1 year Total: 2 years	You get 10 years Friend gets 0 years Total: 10 years
You confess	You get 0 years Friend gets 10 years Total: 10 years	You get 5 years Friend gets 5 years Total: 10 years

The most important finding of the prisoner's dilemma is in
your own self-interest, betrayal is considered the best option.
But that because others, too, are likely to be self-interested,
the outcome for everyone, including you, is worse with that
betrayal.

Beyond its effect on our everyday lives, the reason for looking at game theory here is that in order to propose solutions
that will work beyond local borders, we need to understand
how other countries are likely to play the "game." From the
prisoners' example, it would seem that we are destined to fail
since countries, like people, will choose options to enhance
their own self-interest at the expense of the greater world. The
entire global warming dialogue could be put into this scope as
some countries worry that the economic impact of becoming
carbon-free too quickly will hurt their economies (by making their energy more expensive relative to others). But as we

explore game theory more broadly than the prisoner's dilemma, we'll also see why it might not be as dire as is first seems.

How we play the game, in theory

As we have seen in previous chapters, we humans are often not always as logical or rational in our decision-making process as we might believe. Our emotions and the stories we tell ourselves drive many of our decisions—for better or worse. Some of our decisions look great until the long-term consequences play out, even when we are only playing a game against ourselves. For a moment, though, let's assume that we are always completely rational, making decisions that are best for ourselves, our families, our countries, and the world around us—in that order. On the face of it, it sounds simple enough—until we consider that the decisions that are best for us are oftentimes at odds with each other.

Game theory applies to almost everything when competing for scarce resources. It was developed in 1928 by John von Neumann (1903–1957) and was further refined in 1944 with Oskar Morgenstern (1902–1977) and has broad implication in business, economics, biology, and war—whenever our own actions depend critically on other participants. As different "actors" or "agents" (game theory speak—in this case, you could use "individuals" or "countries") choose different strategies to maximize their own benefit, a "game" is developed where understanding what each actor or agent will do becomes critical to who wins the game. Your decisions therefore depend on the decisions of others. Game theory looks at the interdependence of the strategies. It plays out in far more scenarios than you might imagine—in a competitive world, it applies to many of our choices and decisions. We live in a globally connected world where decisions on one side can make a big difference on the other: jobs, tariffs, taxes, and monetary policy in other countries have a big impact on your wealth and jobs.

But most times in life, the game is unlike the prisoner's dilemma. We have knowledge of how others will play their game. And because human interactions are not limited to a single iteration as shown in the prisoner's dilemma, a complex form of game arises where past moves of others give us clues to how they will act in the future, just as with Bayes's theorem. We assign probabilities to outcomes based on how others will play. Due to this, in a game where everyone cooperates, very often, an incentive accrues to the person who "betrays" or "cheats." In other words, cheating seems like the right payoff, as long as you're the only one and you don't get caught. From the relatively innocuous to the more dangerous, this applies to many areas of your life. Let's look at a number of examples from the real world to see how it plays out.

Driving in the carpool lane. Carpool lanes are intended to remove traffic from the road by encouraging more people per vehicle and thus fewer single-occupant vehicles. If everyone obeys this rule, the overall system is also better for everyone, including single-occupant vehicles, but the commute time is fastest for carpoolers. If one single-occupant vehicle "cheats" and drives in the carpool lane, that person will "win" a faster commute along with the carpoolers, since the carpool lane is faster. But if many single-occupant vehicles cheat, the carpool lane becomes less of an advantage for carpoolers, resulting in fewer people carpooling and more cars on the road.

Drugs or doping in sports. If no one takes performance-enhancing drugs, the overall system is better because no one experiences the dangerous side effects of the drugs. But due to the incentives to win in sports, the payoff is extremely high for a person or team that gains an advantage. Performance-enhancing drugs therefore seem to some to be worth the risk. Lance Armstrong is a prime example. He was long considered the best in the world at cycling, dually convincing the world that he was the poster child of no drugs in sports (because if others took them, he would lose the advantage) while simultaneously taking performance-enhancing drugs. It was the ultimate in hypocrisy, and his fall from grace was catastrophic. I know that I wanted to believe in him and his hero's journey—overcoming cancer to reign supreme at the top of the cycling world. I *did* believe in him right up until the end... and then felt devasted in betrayal.

Military spending. If no country spent money on weapons—nuclear or otherwise—that money could instead be used to benefit the greater society. But if one country chooses to spend on its military and others do not, then that country gains an advantage in military superiority. That creates risk, either perceived or real, for any country not investing in its military. This in turn forces other countries to spend on military to gain parity or create a deterrent to attack, especially if a deemed superior power signals its intent to invade. Many of the chess moves by governments around the world could be thought of in this context, including the current escalation of North Korea's military in response to a feeling that if a dictator could be removed in Iraq, it could happen in North Korea.

Game theory and its implications apply to many of our most contentious societal debates, all arising from the same core issue: in group dynamics, what might be better for one person often is worse for the group. This is why gun control, global warming, currency manipulation, global trade and tariffs, or the race for artificial intelligence superiority become such thorny issues.

Fortunately, as I've said, we rarely play a game just once. If a game is played over and over, and you realize how your opponent plays the game, you are likely to change your strategy. Watching how the game is played when the same participants repeatedly play against each other with different strategies gives a better view into the complexity of relationships and various strategies that drive cooperation and trust.

Artificial intelligence has obvious, important implications for this—deep learning systems, specifically, where multiple AI agents are required to work together or to compete to achieve a desired goal. But what if, instead of a computer playing a computer to achieve a desired goal, the computer played a human? The AI running through all the possible strategies while at the same time forecasting your next move in a way that would defeat us every time?

Play it again, and again

Robert Axelrod, an American scientist best known for his interdisciplinary work on the evolution of cooperation, researched the "iterated prisoner's dilemma." He set up a computer tournament to examine the strategies that had the best outcomes when playing others. The game follows the different strategies participants use once they know the outcome of their opponent's betrayal or cooperation. Some of the more well-known strategies for the game include:

- Always cooperate—No matter what the competitor does.
- Always betray—No matter what the competitor does.
- Tit for tat—Cooperate in the beginning and then copy what the opponent did in their last move.
- Spiteful—Cooperate until an opponent betrays and then always betray.
- Mistrust—Betray first, then copy opponent's moves.

In each of these strategies, you can see some very human responses or personas. They're celebrated or vilified in our popular culture as well. On one side, we've got Gordon Gekko, the archetypical corporate raider in the 1987 film *Wall Street*, who famously said, "The point is, ladies and gentlemen, that greed, for lack of a better word, is good. Greed is right, Greed works. Greed clarifies, cuts through and captures the evolutionary spirit." On the other side, we've got George Bailey, from the 1946 movie *It's a Wonderful Life*, who epitomizes selflessness throughout the movie and is rewarded through positive relationships and a life lived well. Beyond the movies, we see this in our everyday lives as people we trust, through good interactions, receive an advantage in relationship building. With those people, we are still at risk if they choose to later betray us, but a social contract develops where we feel we know that they can be trusted. We get more done in these relationships and feel better about them. We choose to play the game very differently—or not at all—with others who are deemed untrustworthy.

Playing out the strategies against each other through computers, you can also determine which strategies are more effective than others. For example, tit for tat is a fairly simple strategy where one cooperates in the beginning and then copies the move of its competitor. By doing so, it seeks cooperation and continues to cooperate until a competitor does otherwise. If a competitor chooses to betray at some point down the road, it also betrays, only cooperating again if the competitor cooperates first, which is similar to forgiveness in our own lives. This strategy seemed to win against most other strategies. Survival, it seems, at least in a computer simulation, is enhanced by cooperation.

Axelrod's groundbreaking work, *The Evolution of Cooperation*, was originally published in 1984 and has since been built on significantly, shedding light on how trust and reciprocity drives human evolution and relationships. Long-term winning strategies seem to be based on cooperation. An evolutionary bias for cooperation means that although it does not always feel that way, humans acting together in mutual interest should be able to solve our greatest challenges. The cost of not doing so is highest of all: we will likely not survive as a species.

There is an additional area that we should explore, though. Unlike in a computer simulation, in life, the players (us) do not stick with one strategy over the course of our lives. Based on how others play the game, we are constantly modifying our own strategies, copying those of people we respect and changing our minds about how to play our game based on incentives and penalties. That means that it would be unlikely, in a human game, for a single strategy to win forever.

A simple thought experiment shows why. Consider an imaginary world where there was no conflict. Humanity had agreed through mutual reciprocity, trust, and cooperation to abolish all wars. In that imaginary world, society would rid itself of death and destruction from conflict. The prize for all inhabitants would be a world of peace and love. Weapons and the cost of those weapons would no longer be needed. But if a world like that existed, the prize to the power hungry for betrayal would be much higher: a case would be where one country secretly amasses weapons to easily invade and take over all countries because those inhabitants would be unable to defend themselves. And because of that increased payoff, betrayal becomes more likely.

Strategies are therefore in continual flux. A strategy like cooperation wins until such time as it becomes dominant.

Then it is exploited by a selfish or defecting strategy to win for a time by taking advantage of the dominant strategy. At times, even though it feels unjust, the cheaters win. Over time, though, if enough cheaters win, they find themselves isolated and exposed and they are then in turn exploited by cooperative strategies that then rule the day. The process continues to repeat upon itself over and over. This ebb and flow of the right strategy for the right time is a constant in our lives, back and forth like the changing of tides.

This lens is useful at looking at our world today. The world order, largely intact since the end of the World War II, seems to be breaking down. Capitalism, and its relentless march towards progress, allowed many to win. Although no system is perfect, the rules by which capitalism operated were well regarded and understood. You could expect that if you made a big bet and were wrong, you would be wiped out—but if you were right, your hard work, ingenuity, or risk taking would be rewarded. In game theory, we could call this a dominant cooperative strategy, and it dominated for the better part of the twentieth century. The rise of fiat currencies that could be manipulated domestically and the bailout in 2008 changed that strategy to one where the players whose bad bets caused the crisis, instead of being wiped out, were rewarded handsomely. Capitalism's long-dominant cooperative strategy was replaced by a non-dominant strategy, crony capitalism, where the cheaters won.

Perhaps, because it seems that there is a bias for cooperation most of the time, we will find a way to bring harmony to our world over time. With the will of the many, and the right incentive structures, societies might just be able to find a way to limit their exposure to the negative effects of non-cooperation.

The new rules

The right incentive structures might be more possible than we think as we move into the future. Many existing incentive structures change in a world of abundance thanks to technology. The most important elements of our human "games" at their core are about chasing scarce or finite resources—for example, historically, winning an economic advantage in energy came down to scarcity of low-cost fossil fuels. We want to win more of the share, or at least not get hurt by the moves of others.

With abundance comes price deflation. This is simple supply-and-demand economics: the more abundant something is, the more likely it is that its price falls. Abundance changes our perception and economic theory so much that sometimes we do not even recognize something's value anymore, especially when that abundance can be created for free or almost free. Take oxygen. Without it, we stop breathing and die. By that fact alone, it is probably the most valuable thing in our lives. But it is also abundant, making up about 21 percent of the atmosphere, and because it is so abundant, it is free. It would be hard to imagine any business coming up with a very successful model that charged us for the air we breathe (unless, that is, we pollute our world and clean air becomes scarce).

Now consider all the things technology is, and will soon be, making abundant. Things that are incredibly valuable but because of abundance fall in price precipitously.

In a world where technology is concurrently driving deflation and abundance, maybe eventually, one of the forcing functions that makes cooperation more likely to stick is the very fact that there will not be a large economic incentive to "cheat" or "betray"—abundance minimizes the payoff.

Or maybe we should attempt to create an economic system that works that way.

10

A CALL
TO ACTION

"Every company that was designed to have success in the twentieth century is designed to fail in the twenty-first century."

Salim Ismail, author of *Exponential Organizations*, said that to an audience of the Young Presidents' Organization members at a conference that I organized. Ismail understands exponential technologies and helps businesses build a framework for implementing them. Ismail didn't say that the older institutions necessarily *would* fail. But he told us that it is a rare exception in history when a monopoly company of the past does what is necessary to stay relevant in the future.

I thought of all of the examples of companies current and past who couldn't or didn't make the transition. The average thirty-three-year tenure of companies on the S&P 500 list is forecasted to shrink to just twelve years by 2027 due to technology. It makes sense—transition requires long-term thinking. It requires going against the grain of where the current market and profits are. Bets on the future are invariably big bets against where the market is today. To make that bet in light of what investors and stakeholders want you to do to satisfy their immediate short-term needs requires bold leadership and time.

We have looked at many examples of companies that didn't make the right bet, including Kodak, Blockbuster, and Sears. Microsoft might prove to be an example of a success in transition, but for every Microsoft, there is a graveyard of companies that couldn't or wouldn't make the transition. Ironically, one of the reasons Microsoft was able to make that step was because ValueAct Capital, an activist investor, took board seats, understanding the need to support management in its longer-term thinking to allow the transition.

The data is clear in companies, where the cost of not investing in the future is death, but what about some of our biggest institutions that we do not allow to fail? Specifically, the ones like education, healthcare, government. Wouldn't those institutions suffer from the blind spots that allowed technology to change the game for leading companies? And if those institutions are larger, doesn't it make sense that they would be more stuck in the status quo model of delivery, and therefore at greater risk? The difference is that our own governments and institutions define the rules by which we all play the game. If they are the most unlikely to see how those rules need to change or have the courage to take the bold leadership that is needed, we could all be frogs boiling in a pot, not realizing that the heat is being turned up until too late.

But, really, it is not "them." The same thing that allows our best and brightest companies to become irrelevant exists in every one of us. Whether it is sunk-cost bias, confirmation bias, or a host of other biases. Whether it is the overwhelming need to belong that drives us also to divide. Whether it is our short-term thinking with each of us at the centre of our own universe, or game theory that makes us cooperate or betray depending on the incentive or punishment. Whether it is the stories that we tell ourselves, so strongly reinforced in our minds that we miss the very thing biting at our nose.

It is all of them—together. In each and every one of us.

Why would our government institutions be exempt from the flaws of thinking common to all people? The same wiring of our biological computers (our brains) creates exceptionality in our species but also mistakes. That pattern recognition locks us into a path that makes us blind to signposts that don't match our view of the world. Information growth and the rate of change will only accelerate from here, and in a world that is changing so fast, it is not reasonable to expect those in government to be any less vulnerable than we are—even if they set the rules.

It is not that there isn't conversation. All over the world, measures are being explored to try to deal with the problem of rising inequality. But the solutions proposed so far only serve to drive further division, because they fail to recognize the primary reason for that rise in inequality. Economic dogma gives us a false choice from frameworks built for a time before technology, when the world operated differently. Not seeing any other option, we lock into one economic framework or another and defend our position at all costs. And as positions becomes entrenched, we become blind to potential solutions that could save us, just like Kodak missing the digital camera.

Two ways forward

Remember that, according to Ray Dalio, there are only four levers governments can pull to escape debt crises. The current debt burden is so large that any long-term solution must deal with it, so we will categorize the proposed solutions by how they attempt to use one of the four ways to escape the debt burden:

1. Austerity—spending less

2. Debt defaults/restructuring

3. The central bank printing money or other guarantees

4. Transfers of money from those who have more than they need to those who have less (much higher taxes for the rich)

There has been very little mention of the first two levers. As we covered in chapter 1, because of deflation, austerity would create a vicious feedback cycle and a collapse in asset prices, combined with lower employment that would result in debt defaults or restructuring. Because of that, austerity (lever 1) and debt defaults and restructuring (lever 2) are inextricably linked. Whether we start with restructuring or austerity is immaterial; debt will need to be restructured. It is also the most painful for society to bear in the short term, so that might be why there is virtually no dialogue on either of these solutions.

Paradoxically, the debt in the world is already so high that it's not just austerity that would set off an unwind of asset prices and vicious feedback cycle. Slowing growth alone could set off this chain reaction, since the debt becomes unserviceable without fast-enough growth.

Perhaps that is why almost all current proposals today land in two overarching camps on opposing sides of the political spectrum: on one side, those that use lever 3, and on the other side, those that use lever 4. The solutions in them are largely similar in their outcomes but have many different forms. Let's look at the two sides one at a time.

Continued low or negative interest rate environment, central bank printing, modern monetary theory, or other guarantees to keep the party going

The greatest irony of this camp is that it has the highest belief in a free-market economy and capitalism but at the same time doesn't realize that free-market capitalism is not what is happening today.

Many of the current policies around the world could be categorized here, along with many other proposals on the table. When you hear about central bank easing or stimulus, think of this camp. Negative interest rates, modern monetary policy, printing money and driving it into hands of spenders, national and local tax cuts to increase spending—it doesn't matter what you name it or what form it takes, all of these solutions keep the party going by driving more debt. It really doesn't matter if that debt is government, corporate, or personal. It all juices the economy or parts of the economy in the short term while pushing more pain in the longer term.

In the short term, this approach can be successful because people feel richer—that is, until the bill is due. As we see in businesses that fail to transition to a new economic reality, it takes bold leadership to do what is needed for the long term, because the short-term pain is too great. But as a by-product of not taking bold action for the long term, the business is forced into bankruptcy later. I call this the kick-the-can-down-the-road strategy—or rearranging the deck chairs on the *Titanic*. Another way of looking at this strategy is "growth at any cost to society."

A day will come, probably sooner than later, when we realize that the only thing driving our economies is the explosion of debt. If governments need to run huge deficits with extremely low interest rates for fear of growth failing, even in economies that are running at near full employment, imagine how the debt and deficits explode in a recession or depression when the economy falters. Once bond holders determine that governments have little ability to repay or service the debt, the risk premium (or interest rates) on the debt will rise. Sure, governments can monetize and make their currencies worthless, but as other central banks monetize as well, the strategy itself becomes irrelevant.

As we have seen throughout this book, this strategy has only one endgame: 1) higher inequality, 2) people losing hope in the system due to not being able to make ends meet, 3) more polarization, 4) a rise of leaders that use the polarization to create "us versus them" narratives to consolidate power, and 5) commonplace revolution and wars. This solution, in the end, is a dissolution.

Higher taxes on the wealthy, guaranteed basic income

This line of thinking in politics is the liberal/socialist/communist camp. It goes by the principle that the system should be fair for the disadvantaged, so we must tax the wealthy more to pay for the services to the poor.

All of the solutions in this bucket require wealth transfers and, because of that, they are deeply unpopular to many of those with wealth. It is hard to see the money that you believe that you have earned because of your ingenuity or hard work go to others who you deem not to have worked as hard. The argument from those who have wealth is that the higher the tax rate on the wealthy, the more disincentive there is to take risks, innovate, and be a strong contributor to society.

One of the more prominent proposals in this camp is universal basic income. In policy circles around the world, it is getting serious airtime. The idea is simple in premise: raise taxes on the wealthy to give a minimum basic income whether people work or not, topping people up if they work to a maximum amount but also not requiring them to work for their wage.

The idea is hardly new; various proposals date back hundreds of years. In theory, it sounds reasonable. Even for the most ardent capitalist, it could be self-serving. Capitalism collapses in a world where there are no buyers. Job losses and income inequality will reduce the number of people who can participate in the economy. At some point along that continuum of fewer people participating in the economy, the math doesn't work, and the system collapses anyway. That means that even though universal basic income sounds radical to some, it is at least an alternative to that outcome.

On execution, it becomes much more difficult. Universal basic income is essentially a version of wealth transfer. Beyond the traditional arguments from the right that it disincentivizes work and, as a result, incentivizes people to get paid for nothing, there is a cornucopia of additional challenges because of the complexity in determining the right wage. How would government differentiate wages by needs—choosing to live in one city versus another, for example, because of varying costs of living? What if someone chose to live in an expensive city because the opportunities for jobs were higher there but still couldn't find a job—would the basic income be higher for that person? What about people with disabilities or dependents?

Determining the right amount of basic income differentiated for needs becomes difficult to reasonably achieve—especially since the higher the subsidy, the higher the tax on the wealthy, in turn creating a powder keg of division with each side believing they are being taken advantage of.

The most important problem with the solution, though, is simply this: it does not deal with the root cause. Deflation is being caused by technology and, because of that, it will ride the same exponential wave that technology does. That means that the rate of deflation (without printing more money) will only accelerate from here. The abundance that technology provides us doesn't require net new jobs around the world. It obliterates the work and the jobs we already have. That negative effect on jobs will accelerate globally. By cementing in a dual class society, we only ignore the underlying structural change that caused it in the first place. Ignoring that underlying reason is likely to create even more division.

Who's controlling the money?

Both of the above solutions don't consider that since global debt is already so high and expanding quickly, a reset of debt is needed in any truly viable solution. That reset will likely be painful and could erase vast fortunes overnight while also creating new ones. Similar resets have happened in the past. There will be winners and losers depending on where bets are placed.

In addition to this, both of the above solutions rely on a central function of government in setting monetary policy and controlling the underlying value of money, giving it power to drive stimulus to an economy when it needs it. But controlling the value of money can lead to abuse of power—especially if the currency is underlying other currencies.

Just as game theory predicts, we care about our own needs first. Domestic issues always take precedent over international ones, which means a system that is controlled by one nation and is the backbone of all other currencies might work for a time—until the country's domestic issues force it to unilaterally deliver economic benefit to the nation in control of the currency while hurting all others. Once trust is broken in that exchange, game theory predicts actions by other countries will encourage the growth of their own currencies—and all hell breaks loose because international cooperation is lost.

In fact, as we have discussed, many of the same actions with each country devaluing their own currency in an attempt to win the trade game in the early 1900s sowed the seeds of discontent that led to World War II. Vowing not to repeat those mistakes that led to mass unemployment, authoritarianism, and World War II, leaders of the world came together in 1944 to establish Bretton Woods—a framework for global cooperation. A key construct of Bretton Woods was an agreed-upon international monetary system where all countries tied exchange rates to the price of gold and the US dollar; the US dollar became the primary currency of the world and the US dollar was tied to gold through a fixed exchange rate. The new rules established trust in an international framework that allowed global trade to expand and increased global prosperity because it meant that countries could not artificially manipulate their currencies at will.

Again, as game theory predicts, the agreement showed that when countries work together with a clear understanding of the rules, prosperity was enhanced for all. But in 1971, the United States unilaterally terminated a critical aspect of the system—the conversion of the US dollar to gold—and with that change created a system where the US dollar, a fiat currency subject to domestic agenda, was the backbone of the world's economic order. From here, Bretton Woods effectively ended. Since the US dollar became the primary currency of the world without a peg to gold, it gave the US tremendous influence in global affairs. It also enabled a single country to change the rules by printing more currency, and therefore set the stage to return to where we are now, where each country manipulates its currency for political gain while worsening a framework for fair trade.

Bitcoin (and other cybercurrencies) is an attempt at a solution. The promise of Bitcoin was to create a system that was decentralized in nature, unable to be manipulated by anyone—including governments. As we have seen, money follows the rules of supply and demand; the US dollar goes up in value as demand for it increases relative to supply. Governments can change or manipulate this natural dynamic by increasing supply—printing more money, which lowers the value of their currency relative to others. Bitcoin attempts to change that dynamic by forever fixing supply at twenty-one million Bitcoins. In addition to that, it creates a peer-to-peer ledger without any central control: the blockchain. As an open, distributed ledger, it offers security and trust by verifying transactions with consensus instead of through a central authority.

Although the blockchain that Bitcoin sits on has never been hacked, transactions are difficult, which has slowed widespread adoption as a payment alternative. In addition to that, storage of Bitcoins or other cryptocurrencies (wallets) has been prone to cyberattack or loss, creating a different form of risk. But even with risk and current high volatility, citizens in some parts of the world have less risk in holding Bitcoin than their own currency. The value can be moved across borders seamlessly or used as a payment mechanism when currency fails. In Venezuela today, for example, Bitcoin is already acting as a lifesaving currency for those who have it, as it is a much more secure payment medium than the local currency.

Bitcoin's high volatility is often used as an example of why it cannot be trusted as a global payment mechanism. Bitcoin *is* volatile; it lost 30 percent of its value in 2018, only to rise over 100 percent in the first six months of 2019. But that volatility must be put in context. The inflation rate on the bolívar, Venezuela's local currency, was 1.8 million percent in 2018. Having the choice, even in 2018, I would much rather lose 30 percent on my Bitcoin than 1.8 million percent on my bolívar.

The simple solution

There is a principle in philosophy called Occam's razor: a simpler solution is more likely to be correct than a complex one. It makes intuitive sense. Complexity makes us prone to error. As the number of assumptions in coming up with a hypothesis increases, the chances increase that one or more of those assumptions are wrong. To that end, I am going to propose what might be considered the simplest solution of all. So simple, in fact, that it will be hard to imagine.

What if the natural order of things was permitted?

What if, instead of trying to stop deflation at all costs, we embrace it? As technology spreads, deflation happens at the rate it should. Deflation becomes something celebrated because it means that we are getting more for less. We allow ourselves to accept abundance. Along that continuum, as technology removes jobs and fewer overall jobs are needed, prices will keep falling, allowing those who lose jobs a way to share in the benefit of technology abundance without massive transfers of wealth. If technology-driven price declines continue to the point of something becoming free, we let that happen, too. People will no longer have to be on an endless treadmill to pay for things that are constantly rising in price. As hard as that might be for us to accept, because it is such a radical change to the way things are today, it seems to me that it is the only real choice we have.

It is hard to imagine this because we have grown up in a world where these choices did not exist. Where technology deflation was only in isolated pockets of our economies instead of throughout. Where we could count on training people into new jobs and industries not impacted by the changes and continue on the same path that drove prosperity in a different time. That same path is impossible to imagine going forward, with technology soon underpinning almost everything we do.

It is easy to dismiss it out of hand, because we are trapped in a system where we don't know what we would do with ourselves if we didn't have jobs. Our careers are far more important to us than just the income that they bring. Our careers become part of the story of who we are—with our relationships and social status (our "us") often coming from our jobs. For that reason, even if the facts are inescapable, that most of these jobs will be better done by technology, we bury our heads in the sand. The fear of a future without those jobs and self-worth that they bring stops us from imagining a better world in which they might not even be required.

Consider this alternative: allowing abundance without the jobs might actually open an entirely new enlightenment era where we have time to enjoy the benefits that technology brings.

A true capitalist system could work well in that environment because there would still be an incentive to work harder and innovate. Prices of all things would fall, yes, but those creating value would be paid for their value creation—at a rate that matched the new realities of supply and demand and our digital world. We still line up for the newest iPhone even while our service providers let us have older models for free, after all. But those who lose out in our societies would be less at risk. As an entire infrastructure needed to support more jobs to support price inflation resulting from monetary easing is removed, the cost of entitlement programs is removed with it. It becomes much cheaper to live, and thus the burden to those working drops.

In the end, the trend is already clear and foretells a different way of living. It only matters how we get there. The deflationary aspect of technology is too great a force and it will eventually overwhelm even the greatest efforts to stop it. Those efforts to stop it, and the second-order consequences of that fight to halt deflation, will look insane to future generations because that fight will bring on revolutions and wars that burn the existing system to the ground. Allowing that to happen seems insanely irresponsible, since humanity might also forever lose the opportunity to have the kind of social uplift that is possible with technology.

The solution I'm proposing, while simple in theory, has a number of potential limitations. For one thing, would governments around the world allow it to happen? Governments and central banks exert tremendous influence on their economies and citizens with their ability to control money supply. It is not likely that they would voluntarily give up that control to a new world currency that is unable to be manipulated. Without that manipulation of currencies, the natural trend of technology deflation would already be clear.

Another such limitation is that a solution could not be rolled out in just one country. It would need to be rolled out in a coordinated effort internationally, since with trade, one country alone taking this action would be at a disadvantage to other countries still manipulating their currencies.

While I am sure that governments will not voluntarily give up control of their currencies, if there is not a coordinated international effort on a Bretton Woods type of framework that establishes rules around currency exchange rates, it will happen regardless—just in a different way. Remember, a currency only holds value because of the deemed trust we have in it. Beyond that, it is just a piece of paper with faces and numbers on it. That trust is just an agreed upon exchange of value and that government will keep its promises. That trust is compromised if governments do not keep their promises— even if they pretend to by changing the value of the paper the promise is written on. The more that trust is eroded, the more likely that an alternative currency becomes a more trusted mechanism. That alternative—whether Bitcoin or something different—could emerge quickly.

The digital and distributed nature of Bitcoin allows it to benefit from a network effect (which was discussed in chapter 2) with each additional user enhancing its value. As more users trust the system, more trust accretes to the system. Although it is hard to imagine it surpassing any of the main currencies, that reality could easily change tomorrow as more currencies come under pressure; the by-product of that pressure increases the value of Bitcoin or Bitcoin type of network. In other words, what starts as a way for citizens in Venezuela and other regions of the world to escape crushing currency devaluation could jump from country to country and easily build to a point where it becomes the de facto standard of trust.

But what do I know? Even though I think I am aware of my own vulnerabilities in judgment and biases and do my best to correct for them, I am only human, subject to the same flaws and errors as all of us. My solution is only one idea in a sea of many. Perhaps no one solution could work in isolation, and perhaps no solution could be implemented all at once. Maybe solutions need to be brought together through a series of steps to transition our economic foundations to something that works for a future that will predominantly be driven by technology.

That is why I am asking you.

It is clear that something must be done. But because the issues are so complex and thorny in nature, it is easy to put our heads in the sand and hope others will solve them. Trust me, I know. I have myself been sitting on the sidelines, talking about the same thing for about ten years and watching as resentment and polarization in our societies grow. I wrote this book not because I had any desire to but because I grew tired of a lack of real debate about the core issues and solutions and am increasingly worried about world conflict if we don't act. About the world we will pass to our children.

I wrote this book to get us all talking and thinking—and asking the big questions.

Asking big questions is sometimes more powerful than the solution itself because it inspires knowledge of the world to solve it and, as such, brings diverse ways of solving problems. An example of asking a big question is the Ansari X Prize, launched in 1996 by Peter Diamandis, in which twenty-six teams from all over the world competed for a prize of $10 million to create a private spacecraft that was capable of carrying three passengers into sub-orbital space two times within two weeks. Those teams spent more than $100 million, developed breakthroughs, and launched a new space race which we are seeing the benefits of today. Since that time, other crowdsourced competitions have been used to develop breakthroughs in everything from healthcare, to creating better algorithms to find dark matter, to cleaning our oceans. One of the key attributes of crowdsourcing is that it is open to participation; it allows ideas and contribution to come from anywhere and anyone. Those solutions are often far better than anything that could have been imagined by experts in a field.

The internal debate to write this book was derived from the most important lesson in my life, which also came from my greatest tragedy—the sudden loss of my brother. I do my best to live my life with that lesson as a north star, guiding every relationship, and every decision.

That lesson: our lives are defined by the positive impact we have on others.

We are all driven by that love and, when it shows up, that love is what we remember. That is what endures. How those people shaped us, impacted us, and made us better. It becomes our responsibility to take their gifts and pass them on.

I have been extraordinarily fortunate in my life to be surrounded by countless people like that—and I am forever grateful for their impact on me.

I encourage you to contribute to the conversation and debate so that we can together design a world that allows for the best in humanity to thrive as we move into an exciting future of abundance. I invite you to continue the conversation at www.thepriceoftomorrow.com.

NOTES

1   Institute for Policy Studies, "Income Inequality," inequality.org/facts/income-inequality.

2   Ray Dalio, *Principles for Navigating Big Debt Crises* (Bridgewater Associates, 2018), page 12.

3   Ray Dalio, *Principles for Navigating Big Debt Crises* (Bridgewater Associates, 2018), page 12.

4   Comments can be found at: "Testimony of Chairman Ben S. Bernanke," nytimes.com/2007/02/14/business/worldbusiness/14i-ht-web.0214fedtext.4594833.html; "The Subprime Mortgage Market," federalreserve.gov/newsevents/speech/bernanke20070517a.htm; "Bernanke: Fed Ready to Cut Interest Rates Again," nbcnews.com/id/22592939/#.XV2kSS3MyfV; and Danielle DiMartino Booth, *Fed Up* (Portfolio, 2017), page 142.

5   Stephen Mihm, "Dr. Doom," *New York Times Magazine*, August 15, 2008.

6   There has been some talk about GDP not including things that we get because of technology and that we must find a way to include those items in GDP. This is specifically the point. If something is free, or almost free, why would we include it in a GDP measure to see how our debt and credit were driving the economy?

7   John Meynard Keynes, *The Economic Consequences of the Peace* (Macmillan & Co., 1919), page 279. Accessed via archive.org/stream/economicconseque00keynuoft#page/n3/mode/2up.

8   Paul Volcker, as quoted by Andrew Ross Sorkin, "Paul Volcker, at 91, Sees 'A Hell of a Mess in Every Direction,'" *New York Times*, October 23, 2018. nytimes.com/2018/10/23/business/dealbook/paul-volcker-federal-reserve.html.

9   Kim Parker, Rich Morin, and Juliana Menasce Horowitz, "The Future of Work in the Automated Workplace," *Looking to the Future, Public Sees an America in Decline on Many Fronts*, Pew Research Center, March 31, 2019. pewsocialtrends.org/2019/03/21/the-future-of-work-in-the-automated-workplace.

10 Ravi Suria, as quoted by Larry Dignan, "Amazon Cash to Run Dry by 2001?" ZDNet, June 23, 2000. zdnet.com/article/amazon-cash-to-run-dry-by-2001.

11 Matt Day and Jackie Gu, "The Enormous Numbers behind Amazon's Market Reach," Bloomberg, March 27, 2019. bloomberg.com/graphics/2019-amazon-reach-across-markets.

12 NFX, "70% of Value in Tech Is Driven by Network Effects," Medium, November 28, 2017. medium.com/@nfx/70-of-value-in-tech-is-driven-by-network-effects-8c4788528e35.

13 Barry Schwartz, "Google's Search Knows about over 130 Trillion Pages," Search Engine Land, November 14, 2016. searchengineland.com/googles-search-indexes-hits-130-trillion-pages-documents-263378.

14 Joseph A. Schumpeter, *Capitalism, Socialism and Democracy* (Routledge, 1994), page 139.

15 Hyman Minsky, *Stabilizing an Unstable Economy* (McGraw Hill Professional, 2008), page 106.

16 Nassim Nicholas Taleb, *Antifragile* (Random House, 2012), page 101.

17 J.B. Sanford, "Argument against Women's Suffrage," California State Archives, Secretary of State Elections Papers, 1911 Special Election. Available at sfpl.org/pdf/libraries/main/sfhistory/suffrageagainst.pdf.

18 Daniel Kahneman, *Thinking, Fast and Slow* (Random House, 2011), page 2.

19 Jeff Bezos, speaking at Re:MARS conference, June 2019. Quoted in "Jeff Bezos Says the True Secret to Business Success Is to Focus on the Things That Won't Change, Not the Things That Will," *Business Insider*, June 6, 2019. businessinsider.com/jeff-bezos-asks-himself-simple-question-when-planning-for-future-2019-6.

20 Kenneth Flamm, "Moore's Law and the Economics of Semi-conductor Price Trends," *Productivity and Cyclicality in Semiconductors* (The National Academies Press, 2004), pages 151–170. doi.org/10.17226/11134.

21 Lucas Mearian, "CW@50: Data Storage Goes from $1M to 2 Cents Per Gigabyte," *Computerworld*, March 23, 2017. computerworld.com/article/3182207/data-storage/cw50-data-storage-goes-from-1m-to-2-cents-per-gigabyte.html.

22 Brad, "How Fast Is 5G vs 4G?" The Droid Guy, September 5, 2019. thedroidguy.com/2019/01/how-fast-is-5g-vs-4g-1084299.

23 Mikhail Chester, Andrew Fraser, Juan Matute, Carolyn Flower, and Ram Pendyala, "Parking Infrastructure," *Journal of the American Planning Association*, 2015, pages 268–286, doi.org/10.1080/01944363.2015.1092879.

24 Statistics Department, National Safety Council, "NSC Motor Vehicle Fatality Estimates," December 2017, nsc.org/portals/0/documents/newsdocuments/2018/december_2017.pdf.

25 Deloitte, "Global Mobile Consumer Survey: US Edition," 2018. www2.deloitte.com/us/en/pages/technology-media-and-telecommunications/articles/global-mobile-consumer-survey-us-edition.html.

26 Wohlers Associates, *Wohlers Report 2018*. wohlersassociates.com/2018report.htm.

27 Katrin Assenmacher and Signe Krogstrup, "Monetary Policy with Negative Interest Rates," International Monetary Fund Working Paper No. 18/191, August 27, 2018. imf.org/en/Publications/WP/Issues/2018/08/27/Monetary-Policy-with-Negative-Interest-Rates-Decoupling-Cash-from-Electronic-Money-46076.

28 Max Roser and Esteban Ortiz-Ospina, "Income Inequality," Our World in Data, October 2016. ourworldindata.org/income-inequality.

29 Institute for Energy Research, "A Primer on Energy and the Economy," February 16, 2010. instituteforenergyresearch.org/uncategorized/a-primer-on-energy-and-the-economy-energys-large-share-of-the-economy-requires-caution-in-determining-policies-that-affect-it.

30 US Department of Energy, "DOE Releases First Annual National Energy Employment Analysis," March 24, 2016. energy.gov/articles/doe-releases-first-annual-national-energy-employment-analysis.

31 John Kraft and Arthur Kraft, "On the Relationship between Energy and GNP," *Journal of Energy and Development*, 1978, pages 401–403.

32 Hannah Ritchie and Max Roser, "Energy Production and Changing Energy Sources," Our World in Data, 2019. ourworldindata.org/energy-production-and-changing-energy-sources.

33 Jeff Tsao, Nate Lewis, and George Crabtree, "Solar FAQs," Sandia National Laboratories, April 20, 2006. sandia.gov/~jytsao/Solar%20 FAQs.pdf.

34 Matt Gray, Sebastian Ljungwaldh, Laurence Watson, and Irem Kok, *Powering Down Coal* (Carbon Tracker, November 2018). carbontracker.org/reports/coal-portal.

35 Lazard, "Levelized Cost of Energy and Levelized Cost of Storage 2018," November 8, 2018. lazard.com/perspective/levelized-cost-of-energy-and-levelized-cost-of-storage-2018.

36 Mark Lewis, *Wells, Wires, and Wheels...* (BNP Paribas, August 2019). docfinder.bnpparibas-am.com/api/files/1094E5B9-2FAA-47A3-805D-EF65EAD09A7F.

37 Jeff Tsao, Nate Lewis, and George Crabtree, "Solar FAQs," Sandia National Laboratories, April 20, 2006. sandia.gov/~jytsao/Solar%20 FAQs.pdf.

38 Land Art Generator, "Total Surface Area Required to Fuel the World with Solar," August 13, 2009. landartgenerator.org/blagi/archives/127.

39 Bill Nussey, "How Much Solar Would It Take to Power the U.S.?" The Freeing Energy Project, July 6, 2018. freeingenergy.com/how-much-solar-would-it-take-to-power-the-u-s.

40 Organization of American States, "Desalination by Distillation," *Source Book of Alternative Technologies for Freshwater Augmentation in Latin America and the Caribbean*, Unit of Sustainable Development and Environment General Secretariat, Organization of American States, 1997. oas.org/usde/publications/Unit/oea59e/ch20.htm.

41 Simon Neubauer, Jean-Jacques Hublin, and Philipp Gunz, "The Evolution of Modern Human Brain Shape," *Science Advances*, January 24, 2018. doi.org/10.1126/sciadv.aao5961.

42 Lucien Febvre and Henri-Jean Martin, *The Coming of the Book* (Verso, 1976).

43 Karl Popper, *Conjectures and Refutations* (Penn, Buckinghamshire, 1965).

44 Isaac Newton, letter to Robert Hooke, February 5, 1675. Available at digitallibrary.hsp.org/index.php/Detail/objects/9792.

45 Voltaire, *Le Siècle de Louis XIV* (1752).

46 Karl Popper, as quoted by Mark Damazer, "*In Our Time*'s Greatest Philosopher Vote," *In Our Time* (BBC 4).

47 "The Babbage Engine," Computer History Museum. computer history.org/babbage.

48 Claude E. Shannon, "A Mathematical Theory of Communication," *Bell System Technical Journal*, 1948.

49 John McCarthy, Marvin Minsky, Nathaniel Rochester, and Claude Shannon, "A Proposal for the Dartmouth Summer Research Project on Artificial Intelligence," August 31, 1955. Available at www-formal.stanford.edu/jmc/history/dartmouth/dartmouth.html.

50 Jack Copeland, "Biography of Turing," AlanTuring.net, July 2000. alanturing.net/turing_archive/pages/Reference%20Articles/Bio%20of%20Alan%20Turing.html.

51 Gatsby Charitable Foundation, "Gatsby Computational Neuroscience Unit," gatsby.org.uk/neuroscience/programmes/gatsby-computational-neuroscience-unit.

52 K. Anders Ericsson, Ralf Th. Krampe, and Clemens Tesch-Römer, "The Role of Deliberate Practice in the Acquisition of Expert Performance," *Psychological Review*, 1993, pages 363–406. projects.ict.usc.edu/itw/gel/EricssonDeliberatePracticePR93.pdf.

53 William Hirst et al., "Long-Term Memory for the Terrorist Attack of September 11," *Journal of Experimental Psychology* (2009). pdfs.semanticscholar.org/89f4/bbaff6e7c289b7836047fbc8d73e7d012711.pdf.

54 George A. Miller, "The Magical Number Seven, Plus or Minus Two," *Psychological Review*, March 1956.

55 Diego Ardila et al., "End-to-End Lung Cancer Screening with Three-Dimensional Deep Learning on Low-Dose Chest Computed Tomography," *Nature Medicine*, 2019, pages 954–961. doi.org/10.1038/s41591-019-0447-x.

56 "'Whoever Leads in AI Will Rule the World,'" RT.com, September 1, 2017. rt.com/news/401731-ai-rule-world-putin.

57 Lord Acton, in a letter to Bishop Mandell Creighton in 1887.

58 Elon Musk, as quoted by Graham Rapier, "'If You Can't Beat Them Join Them,'" *Business Insider*, September 3, 2019. businessinsider.com/elon-musk-humans-must-become-cyborgs-to-compete-with-ai-2019-8.

59 Roy Baumeister and Mark Leary, "The Need to Belong," *Psychological Bulletin*, May 1995, pages 497–529. dx.doi.org/10.1037/0033-2909.117.3.497.

60 Muzafer Sherif, *Group Conflict and Co-operation* (London: Routledge & Kegan Paul Limited, 1966).

61 Frank Outlaw, "Watch Your Thoughts, They Become Words; Watch Your Words, They Become Actions," Quote Investigator, January 10, 2013. quoteinvestigator.com/2013/01/10/watch-your-thoughts.

62 Abraham Maslow, "A Theory of Human Motivation," *Psychological Review* (1943), pages 370–396.

63 Louis Tay and Ed Diener, "Needs and Subjective Well-Being around the World," *Journal of Personality and Social Psychology*, August 2011, pages 354–365. psycnet.apa.org/doiLanding?doi=10.1037%2Fa0023779.

64 Yu-kai Chou, "Octalysis—The Complete Gamification Framework," yukaichou.com/gamification-examples/octalysis-complete-gamification-framework.

65 Adolf Hitler, *Mein Kampf*, trans. Roberto Marco (MVR, 1939), page 139.

66 Stanley Milgram, "The Behavioural Study of Obedience," *Journal of Abnormal and Social Psychology*, October 1963, pages 371–378.

67 Stanley Milgram, "The Perils of Obedience," *Harper's Magazine*, December 1973. harpers.org/archive/1973/12/the-perils-of-obedience.

ABOUT THE AUTHOR

J EFF BOOTH IS a visionary leader who has lived at the forefront of technology change for twenty years. He led BuildDirect, a technology company that aimed to simplify the building industry, for nearly two decades through the dotcom meltdown, the 2008 financial crisis, and many waves of technological disruption.

Jeff has been featured in *Forbes*, TechCrunch, Inc.com, *The Globe and Mail*, BNN, *Fast Company*, *Entrepreneur*, Bloomberg, *TIME*, and *The Wall Street Journal*. In 2015, he was named BC Technology Industry Association's Technology Person of the Year, and in 2016

Goldman Sachs named him among its 100 Most Intriguing Entrepreneurs.

He is a founding partner of OtioLabs; cofounder of NocNoc and addyinvest.com; and serves on the boards of Terramera, SPUD.ca, LlamaZOO, Synthiam, and the Richmond Hospital Foundation, among others.

Jeff has been a Young Presidents' Organization member since 2004, and contributes time as a founding fellow on the Creative Destruction Lab.

www.thepriceoftomorrow.com

Made in the USA
Middletown, DE
20 May 2021

40054905R00139